Do You Remember? The 1960s

An exclusive edition for

for all your gift books and gift stationery

Watford, Herts, U.K. WD19 4BG

ALLSORTED.
for all your gift books and gift stationery

Published in 2016 by Allsorted. Watford, Herts, U.K. WD19 4BG

Compiled by Michael Powell
Illustrations reproduced courtesy of Shutterstock.com
Page 6, Catwalker: page 24, Michele Paccione; page 52, ShestakovV;
page 76, 360b, page 94, Andy Lidstone; page 111, urbanbuzz; at Shutterstock

Concept by Milestone Design
Designed by Joanna Ross at Double Fish Design Ltd

Printed in China

*Every effort has been made to ensure the accuracy of the information contained in this book.
In the unlikely case of queries please contact the compilers via their website www.susannageoghegan.com.*

Introduction

The sixties were cool. Well, you should know because you lived through them. This special decade witnessed the first episode of *Dr Who*, the last live performance from The Beatles and did you know that in 1963 a pint of beer cost the equivalent of just ten pence today?

You could hear The Dave Clark Five, The Animals and Martha and the Vandellas on the radio and watch Peter O'Toole, Susannah York and Rita Tushingham on the big screen. J.P.R. Williams made his International rugby debut, humans landed on the moon and pull tabs appeared on drinks cans. What a great time to be growing up.

Well, that was all a long time ago, but you'd be surprised how many memories you can refresh with a little encouragement. There are 54 quizzes and more than 1,000 questions covering world events, music, films, celebrities, fads and crazes, fashions, comedians, actors, singers, inventions, advertisements, novels, toys, sporting greats, scientific achievements and lots of things that made your sixties childhood unique.

Some of the questions will be easy for you to answer but almost impossible for those without your personal experience. Other questions will call up random memories to make you smile. All those real moments have disappeared but you will always have this book to remind you!

3

Contents

Contents

The Year That Was

1960

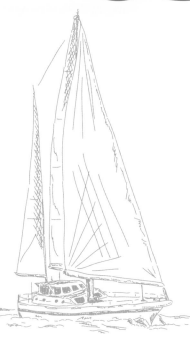

1. Which US politician and future President first announced his candidacy for the Democratic presidential election on 2nd January 1960?

2. Which British Prime Minister told the South African Parliament on 3rd February 1960, 'The wind of change is blowing through this continent. Whether we like it or not, this growth of national consciousness is a political fact'?

3. Which Academy Award-winning Hollywood actress, known for movies such as *The Three Faces of Eve* and for her marriage in 1958 to Paul Newman, received her star on

the Hollywood Walk of Fame on 9th February 1960?

4. Which annual British sporting event was televised in the UK for the first time in March 1960?

5. Which rock and roll star received an honourable discharge from the US Army on 5th March 1960?

6. Which iconic British shoe was made for the first time in Northampton on 1st April 1960?

7. Which member of the British Royal Family was christened on 8th April 1960?

8. Which broadsheet daily newspaper dropped the phrase 'Imperial and Foreign News' from 16th April 1960, replacing it with, 'Overseas News'?

9. Which US rock and roll star was killed in an air crash on 17th April 1960?

10. Which British Royal Wedding took place on 6th May 1960?

11. What was particularly significant about the wedding ceremony?

12. Which English football club won the FA Cup for the fourth successive year on 7th May 1960?

13. What was different about the US 'Stars and Stripes' flag that was hoisted over Philadelphia on 4th July 1960?

14. What record-breaking feat was completed by Englishman, Francis Chichester, in New York on 21st July 1960?

15. Which Mediterranean island gained its independence from the UK on 16th August 1960?

16. Which sport was televised live for the first time in the UK on 10th September 1960, but wouldn't be again for another 23 years?

17. Who began patrolling the streets of London for the first time on 15th September 1960?

18. Which controversial book, banned since 1928 for obscenity, sold 200,000 copies in a single day after it was finally re-published by Penguin Books on 10th November 1960?

19. Which two religious leaders met for the first time in history on 2nd December 1960?

20. What British coin ceased to be legal tender in the UK at midnight on New Year's Eve, 1960?

The Year That Was

1961

1. On 3rd January 1961, Dwight Eisenhower announced that the US had severed diplomatic relations with which nation?

2. Which classic British espionage series was first aired on ITV on 7th January 1961?

3. Who succeeded Dwight Eisenhower as President of the United States on 20th January 1961?

4. Which broadsheet Sunday newspaper was first published on 5th February 1961?

5. Which banknote ceased to be legal tender in the UK on 13th March 1961?

6. Which theatre and resident theatre company was inaugurated for the first time on 20th March 1961?

7. Who was its first director?

8. What were the residents of Washington DC permitted to do for the first time, following the ratification of the Twenty-third Amendment to the US constitution on 29th March 1961?

9. Which classic British two-seater sports car was launched on 3rd April 1961?

10. What were legally permitted to open up shop on the British high street from 1st May 1961?

11. What landmark technological ambition did the US President announce before Congress on 25th May 1961, pledging to see it achieved by the end of the decade?

12. Which Russian cosmonaut became the first human to orbit the Earth on 12th April 1961?

13. Which Russian ballet dancer defected to the West while performing with the Kirov Ballet in Paris on 16th June 1961?

14. Who succeeded Geoffrey Fisher as Archbishop of Canterbury on 27th June 1961?

15. To which international body did the UK apply for membership on 10th August 1961?

16. Work began on which iconic construction in Berlin on 13th August 1961?

17. Which animated animal duo made a comeback on 7th September, 1961, with their first cartoon since 1957?

18. Which British satirical magazine was first published on 25th October 1961?

19. What became available to women on the NHS for the first time from 4th December 1961?

20. What form of home entertainment became available to the people of Ireland for the first time on 31st December 1961?

The Year That Was

1962

1. Which television police drama first aired on the BBC on 2nd January 1962?

2. Which revolutionary political figure was excommunicated by Pope John XXIII on 3rd January 1962?

3. What was featured inside a Sunday newspaper for the first time on 4th February and what was the newspaper?

4. On 21st February 1962, England's most loved prima ballerina embarked upon a legendary artistic partnership with a recently defected Russian ballet dancer. Who were they?

5. What new form of pedestrian crossing confused drivers and pedestrians with its bewildering sequence of flashing and pulsating lights on 2nd April 1962?

6. What form of public transport ran for the last time on the streets of London on 8th May 1962?

7. What form of entertainment opened legally for the first time in the UK in Brighton on 2nd June 1962?

8. Which British band recorded at London's Abbey Road studios for the first time on 6th June 1962?

9. Which brand new British theatre opened on 3rd July 1962, under the artistic direction of Laurence Olivier?

10. Which of Andy Warhol's iconic works premiered in Los Angeles on 9th July 1962?

11. Which iconic British band made their debut at London's Marquee Club on 12th July 1962?

12. Which anti-apartheid South African ANC figure was arrested and charged with incitement to cause rebellion on 5th August 1962?

13. Which Caribbean island gained its independence from the UK on 6th August 1962?

14. Following the dismissal of Pete Best, who joined The Beatles on 16th August 1962?

15. Which long-running inter-collegiate British television quiz show aired for the first time on 21st September 1962?

16. On 5th October 1962, the first in a brand new movie series premiered in London, starring Sean Connery. What was the movie?

17. Following the detection of Soviet missiles under construction in Cuba on 14th October 1962, a 12-day international standoff ensued. Name the crisis.

18. Who hosted the British satirical comedy programme, *That Was the Week That Was*, which first aired on 24th November 1962?

19. On 29th November 1962, Britain and France entered into an agreement to jointly produce which ground breaking new airliner?

20. On Christmas Eve 1964, what did Cuba exchange with the US in return for $53 million worth of food?

The Year That Was

1963

1. Which long-running investigative current affairs programme was launched on Granada television on 7th January 1963?

2. Which leader of the British Labour party died suddenly at the age of 56 on 18th January 1963?

3. Which European Head of State vetoed the British application for entry to the EEC on 29th January 1963?

4. Who was elected the new leader of the Labour Party on 14th February?

5. Which notorious US prison closed its doors for the last time on 21st March 1963?

6. The Beatles released their debut album on 22nd March 1963. What was it called?

7. What did the Beeching Report call for upon its release on 27th March 1963?

8. What did a law passed in New South Wales on 30th March 1963 permit indigenous Australians to do legally for the first time?

9. Which epic movie won the Academy Award for Best Picture on 8th April 1963?

10. Which British football club became the first to win a European trophy at the European Cup Winners' tournament on 15th May 1963?

11. Which British Secretary of State for War resigned on 5th June, admitting he had deceived Parliament over an affair with a London showgirl, who was simultaneously having an affair with a Soviet spy?

12. What was the name of the showgirl involved in the scandal?

13. The first reported disappearance of a teenage girl in Manchester began which notorious serial murder case on 12th July 1963?

14. What happened at a railway bridge near Ledburn, Buckinghamshire in the early hours of 8th August 1963?

15. What did Martin Luther King tell a crowd of 250,000 people from the steps of the Lincoln Memorial in Washington DC on 28th August 1963?

16. Who took over as British Prime Minister following the resignation of Harold Macmillan due to ill health on 19th October 1963?

17. Laurence Olivier took over as artistic director of which new theatre on 22nd October 1963?

18. What news shook the world on 22nd November 1963?

19. Which much-loved and long-running sci-fi series first aired on the BBC on 23rd November 1963?

20. Which Disney movie was first released on 25th December 1963?

The Year That Was

1964

1. Which music show first aired on the BBC on 1st January 1964?

2. Which weekly magazine targeted at teenage girls was first published in the UK on 11th January 1964?

3. What did the US Surgeon General report on 11th January 1964, the first time the US government had made a public admission on the subject?

4. Why did hundreds of screaming fans gather at JFK airport in New York on 7th February 1964?

5. Which banknote was issued in the UK on 21st February for the first time since the Second World War?

6. Why did the Italian government appeal for international help on 27th February 1964?

7. Which royal birth took place on 10th March 1964?

8. Which new town in southern Britain did the British government announce plans to construct on 19th March 1964?

9. What was launched from a ship moored just beyond UK territorial waters off the coast of Felixstowe on 28th March 1964?

10. Which two subcultural youth movements met in violent clashes on Clacton beach on 30th March 1964?

11. Which television channel began broadcasting on 20th April 1964?

12. What store opened on London's Fulham Road on 6th May, the brainchild of designer Terence Conran?

13. What act of non-violent defiance against the war in Vietnam was carried out for the first time in the US on 12th May 1964, by twelve young men at an anti-war rally in New York?

14. Which African Nationalist leader was sentenced to life imprisonment at Robben Island on 12th June 1964?

15. The construction of which iconic London landmark was completed on 15th July 1964?

16. Which British statesman retired from the House of Commons on 28th July 1964, at the age of 89?

17. Which nation was banned from participating in the 1964 Tokyo Olympics on 18th August, on the grounds that their team was racially segregated?

18. Which long-running sports programme first aired on BBC2 on 22nd August 1964?

19. Which Disney movie premiered on 27th August, and would become the first Disney movie to receive an Academy Award nomination for Best Picture?

20. What historic decision was made in the House of Commons on 9th November 1964?

The Year That Was

1965

1. Which twin brothers were arrested on 7th January 1965 on suspicion of running a protection racket in London's East End?

2. Which former British statesman died on 24th January 1965?

3. What was brought to an end within the National Health Service on 31st January 1965?

4. What new record in Association Football was set by Sir Stanley Matthews on 6th February 1965?

5. What appeared on the Canadian flag for the first time on 15th February 1965?

6. Which sharp-tongued, self-deprecating female comedian from New York made her television debut on Johnny Carson's *Tonight Show* on 17th February 1965?

7. Which creature was captured and returned safely to London Zoo on 11th March 1965, thirteen days after its escape?

8. Soviet Cosmonaut Alexey Leonov made history on 18th March carrying out what historic task for twelve minutes?

9. Which two Hollywood musicals swept the boards at the 37th Annual Awards on 5th April 1965?

10. Which football team won the FA Cup on 1st May 1965 for the first time in history?

11. What did the National Trust's 'Enterprise Neptune' project look to protect from its launch on 11th May 1965?

12. What new scheme to ensure road safety was announced in the Commons on 18th June 1965?

13. The notorious Great Train Robber, Ronnie Biggs, escaped from which prison on 8th July 1965?

14. What feature of an Alpine highway was inaugurated by French President Charles de Gaulle and Italian President Giuseppe Saragat on 16th July 1965?

15. How did folk music legend Bob Dylan attract controversy at the Newport Folk Festival in Rhode Island on 25th July 1965?

16. On 1st August 1965, what was banned from being advertised on British television?

17. What significant event occurred at a BP oil platform in the North Sea on 21st September 1965?

18. On 22nd October, a group of African nations pressured the UK to use force if necessary to prevent which African country from declaring its independence?

19. Which British serial killers appeared in court to face murder charges for the first time on 29th October 1965?

20. Which outspoken English social activist founded the National Viewers' and Listeners' Association, a pressure group against offensive media content, on 29th November 1965?

The Year That Was

1. What happened after a US B-52 bomber collided with a military aerial refuelling plane over the town of Palomares, Spain on 17th January 1966?

2. Who was sworn in as President of India on 24th January 1966?

3. Which significant monetary change in the UK was first announced by Chancellor James Callaghan on 1st March 1965, to be effective from 1971?

4. In an interview with the *Evening Standard* on 4th March 1966, who claimed to be 'more popular than Jesus'?

5. What opened its doors to the public on 11th April 1966, offering the first of its kind outside of Africa?

6. A new means of crossing the English Channel was introduced on 30th April 1966. What was it?

7. What did Dr Martin Luther King, Jr. speak out against for the first time on 16th May 1966?

8. What was introduced in the UK for the first time on 29th June 1966 by Barclays Bank?

9. Which UK political party won parliamentary representation for the first time in its 41-year history with the election of Gwynfor Evans on 14th July 1966?

10. A ban on the employment of which category of workers at Euston Station was overturned on 15th July 1966?

11. Which historic football event took place at Wembley Stadium on 30th July 1966?

12. Which bridge, one of the longest road bridges in Europe, was opened in Scotland on 18th August 1966, linking Newport-on-Taye in Fife to Dundee?

13. Which British band performed their last live concert in San Francisco on 29th August 1966?

14. Which of the Great Train Robbers was arrested on 19th September upon his return from Mexico?

15. Which US psychologist founded the League for Spiritual Discovery on 19th September 1966, hoping in the process to legalise the use of LSD on religious grounds?

16. Why did the world's attention turn to a small mining town in South Wales named Aberfan on 21st October 1966?

17. What dramatic scene, now iconic, was aired for the first time during a long-running British television sci-fi series on 29th October 1966, starring William Hartnell and Patrick Troughton?

18. Which album did The Beatles begin recording at Abbey Road Studios on 24th November 1966?

19. Walt Disney died on 15th December 1966, part way through supervising which animated movie?

20. After significant negotiations with the UK and despite pressure from numerous African states, which African state had its move to independence agreed by Harold Wilson on 20th December 1966?

The Year That Was

1967

1. The movie *A Countess From Hong Kong*, which opened on 2nd January 1967, was the last to star which veteran actor?

2. On 12th January 1967, a psychology professor from the University of California became the first person to undergo which post-mortem procedure?

3. Who became leader of the British Liberal Party on 18th January 1967?

4. Which British industry learned that it was to be 90 per cent nationalised on 26th January 1967?

5. On 12th February 1967, a police drugs raid was carried out at Redlands, the Sussex home of which British rock legend?

6. What was pumped ashore for the first time at the East Riding of Yorkshire on 4th March 1967?

7. On 31st March 1967, Jimi Hendrix was taken to hospital after doing what for the first time on stage?

8. Which British song won the Eurovision Song Contest on 8th April 1967?

9. Why was Muhammad Ali stripped of his heavyweight boxing title on 28th April 1967?

10. On 18th May 1967, the Governor of Tennessee finally repealed the Butler Act, which had first come under intense scrutiny during the Scopes Trial of 1925. What had been prohibited in US schools under the terms of the Butler Act?

11. What appeared at the Enfield branch of Barclays Bank on 27th June 1967, the first of its kind in the UK?

12. Which British sports event was broadcast on BBC2 in colour for the first time on 1st July 1967?

13. What was decriminalised by the British Parliament in England and Wales on 4th July 1967?

14. What event was fixed at the last Monday in August for the first time on 28th August 1967?

15. Which national pop radio station was launched in the UK on 30th September 1967?

16. What medical procedure was legalised in the UK under a number of conditions on 25th October 1967?

17. What was launched by the BBC for the first time on 8th November 1967, beginning in Leicester?

18. Why was a ban on the movement of farm animals introduced across England and Wales on 18th November 1967?

19. Why did the appointment of Tony O'Connor as Head Teacher of a Smethwick Primary School make the news on 1st December 1967?

20. Which new airliner was unveiled to the public in Toulouse on 11th December 1967?

The Year That Was

1. Which well-known gardener made his television debut with the BBC on 5ᵗʰ January 1968?

2. What did Harold Wilson's 'I'm Backing Britain' campaign urge people to do on a daily basis, in the name of their country's growth from 8ᵗʰ January 1968?

3. Which Cold War civilian voluntary organisation, designed to take charge in the event of a national emergency such as a nuclear attack, did Prime Minister Harold Wilson announce would be stepped down from 16ᵗʰ January 1968?

4. On 1ˢᵗ February 1968, a US Associated Press photojournalist took what would become a Pulitzer Prize-winning photograph of a young Viet Cong officer. The image was influential in garnering significant support for the anti-war movement. What was happening to the officer in the photograph?

5. What did Cambridge University announce on 24ᵗʰ February 1968 had been discovered by astronomer Jocelyn Bell Burnell?

6. An industrial closure at Baggeridge near Sedgley on 2ⁿᵈ March 1968

ended three centuries of which industry in the Black Country?

7. The Police forces in Oxfordshire, Berkshire and Buckinghamshire amalgamated on 1st April 1968 to form which new force?

8. What did US entrepreneur Robert P. McCulloch purchase on 18th April 1968 and relocate to a city in Arizona?

9. Which new coins were introduced in the UK on 23rd April 1968, in preparation for decimalisation?

10. Which notorious East End mob leaders were arrested in a dawn raid along with 16 other men on 8th May 1968?

11. What was permitted within the Church of Scotland for the first time from 22nd May 1968?

12. Which idiosyncratic US artist was shot and wounded by a radical feminist named Valerie Solanas as he entered his studio on 3rd June 1968?

13. Alec Rose, a fruit merchant from Kent was greeted with a hero's welcome and a knighthood after returning to the UK on 4th July 1968,

following a 354-day adventure. What had he achieved?

14. Which international sporting event took place at Soldier Field in Chicago for the first time on 20th July 1968?

15. What did the 'Fifteen Guinea Special' mark on 11th August 1968?

16. US Marine James Anderson, Jr. was posthumously awarded the Medal of Honor in the US on 21st August 1968. Why was his decoration particularly momentous?

17. Jefferson Airplane was among the acts performing at a counterculture event on 1st September 1968. The festival would become one of England's foremost annual music festivals. Where was it held?

18. What was introduced by the General Post Office on 16th September 1968?

19. New mum, Sheila Thorns, from Birmingham hit the headlines on 2nd October 1968. What made her story newsworthy?

20. Which British rock band, formerly known as the New Yardbirds, made their US debut on 26th December 1968?

The Year That Was

1969

1. Which Australian media baron purchased British tabloid newspaper, *The News of the World* on 2nd January 1969?

2. Which band gave an impromptu performance from their London production company's roof on 30th January 1969, the last time they would perform live together?

3. Which DIY superstore opened its doors for the first time in March 1969, with an inaugural branch in Southampton?

4. Which branch of the London Underground was opened on 7th March 1969?

5. What right was granted to Sikh bus drivers in Wolverhampton on 9th April 1969?

6. What change was made to the voting system in the UK with the passing of the Representation of the People Act on 17th April 1969?

7. Who stepped down as President of France on 28th April 1969?

8. Which British ocean liner made her maiden voyage from Southampton, bound for New York, on 2nd May 1969?

9. A number of spontaneous riots broke out in New York City on 28th June 1969. They would become known as the Stonewall Riots and marked the beginning of what equal rights movement in the US?

10. A royal ceremony took place in Caernarfon, Wales, with a key focus on Prince Charles. What was the purpose of the ceremony?

11. Which town in South Wales was granted city status on 3rd July 1969?

12. Which historic space flight took off on 16th July 1969 watched by millions around the globe?

13. Name the three crew members.

14. Which pre-decimal coin was no longer legal tender in the UK after 1st August 1969?

15. A riot in Derry, Northern Ireland on 12th August 1969, later named the Battle of the Bogside, was regarded as the first in what period of sectarian unrest in the province?

16. Which iconic high street fashion store opened on Kensington High Street in London on 16th September 1969?

17. Which island off the coast of Devon was acquired by the National Trust for preservation and conservation on 28th September 1969?

18. What replaced the 10-shilling-note on 14th October 1969, to an unenthusiastic reception from the British public?

19. In the US on 12th November 1969, an independent investigative journalist named Seymour Harsh broke a story about an atrocity that took place during the war in Vietnam. What was the atrocity?

20. On 25th November 1969, how did John Lennon demonstrate his opposition to the support given by the British government to the US war with Vietnam?

Sixties British

TELEVISION

1. Which popular music panel show ran throughout the decade from its first airing in 1959, and involved a panel of celebrity guests who would review new releases, judging them to be either a 'hit' or a 'miss'?

2. Which ITV series was a vehicle for one of Britain's best loved comedy duos and aired from 1961 until 1968, when the pair moved to the BBC?

3. Charles Hawtrey, William Hartnell and Bernard Bresslaw were among a large cast of actors to star in which sitcom about life as a young army conscript serving out National Service, which aired on ITV until 1961?

4. Which television spy-thriller, first aired on ITV in 1961, starred Ian Hendry, Patrick Macnee, Honor Blackman and Diana Rigg?

5. Which much-loved comedy series ended in 1961, starring Tony Hancock, Sid James, Hattie Jacques and Kenneth Williams?

6. What name was given to an anthology of self-contained sitcoms that ran from 1961 throughout the decade?

7. Which iconic television sci-fi series first aired on the BBC in 1963, produced by Verity Lambert and originally conceived as an educational

vehicle within which to explore scientific ideas and principles?

8. Which 1964 documentary series examined the First World War and was narrated by Michael Redgrave?

9. Which weekly documentary series first aired on the BBC in 1964, with an opening episode that examined Buckminster Fuller?

10. Which sitcom first aired in 1964, starring James Bolam, Bob Ferris, Thelma Chambers and Audrey Collier? It would spawn a *Whatever Happened To* sequel in the 1970s.

11. Which television game show was first aired in 1965 and pitched two celebrity teams against each other to baffle their opponents with three definitions of obscure words?

12. Which family game show, involving pitching teams against each other over a series of assault courses, first aired on the BBC in 1966?

13. Which television comedy show first aired in 1967 and featured early performances from the Python team, and from other stars of the future such as David Jason?

14. Which television game show

featured a cross bow attached to a camera and was hosted by Bob Monkhouse from 1967 until 1975?

15. Which sitcom about a hapless group of men in the Home Guard during the Second World War was written by David Croft and Jimmy Perry and first aired on the BBC in 1968?

16. Which long-running BBC programme first aired from Oxford Botanical Gardens in 1968, hosted by Ken Burras?

17. Which police drama ran throughout the decade, looking at life at a London police station from the point of view of a sympathetic local constable played by Jack Warner?

18. Which BBC series looked at vacation destinations and was hosted by Cliff Michelmore from its first appearance in 1969 until 1986?

19. Which British sitcom, written by Carla Lane, about two young women sharing a flat in Liverpool first aired in 1969 and ran for a decade?

20. Which groundbreaking British sketch show first aired on the BBC in 1969?

Complete these slogans

ADVERTISING

1. _____adds brightness to cleanness and whiteness.

2. Look your loveliest with _____.

3. One, two, three, four reasons why Julie Andrews likes_____!

4. Come alive! You're in the _____Generation!

5. _____makes the most of a man.

6. A _____ works wonders, works wonders, works wonders.

28

COMPLETE THESE SLOGANS – ADVERTISING

7. Talk it over with the man from_____. He lives nearby.

8. Your skin needs_____.

9. You can be sure of _____ ____.

10. The happiest people you meet in the morning get their sunshine out of a box. And the box is_____.

11. Don't forget the_____, Doreen!

12. The_____ are on me.

13. A boy and his _____turns a boy's world into a man's world.

14. _____makes clothes springy-soft!

15. You're never alone with a_____.

16. Go to work on _____.

17. Did you_____ your teeth today?

18. Get away in a_____.

19. It is the bounce, the natural bounce and you get it with _____ shampoo!

20. And all because the lady loves_____.

Sixties FASHION

1. What hairstyle was made popular by The Beatles?

2. What was Ursula Andress wearing in *Dr No* that was to become so iconic she later described it as having 'made me into a success' and that would enjoy enormous popularity during the decade?

3. Which iconic clothing store opened in Kensington in 1964, selling a range of tight-sleeved dresses in earthy colours, run by Polish-born designer Barbara Hulanicki?

4. Which British designer ran a store on London's King's Road, called Bazaar?

5. With which iconic single item of women's fashion from the decade was Bazaar's owner most closely associated?

6. In 1964, French designer, André Courrèges, launched a boot for women that would become one of the decade's most iconic pieces of footwear. What was it?

7. What were fashionable women, beatniks and revolutionaries most commonly wearing on their heads during the decade?

8. Who was the German supermodel who appeared on more magazine covers

than anyone else through the 1960s and commanded a salary of $10,000 a day at the height of her career?

9. What colourful means of decorating fabric was popular in the later 1960s, particularly among the counterculture movement in the US?

10. What were love bead-clad hippies choosing to wear on their legs by 1967?

11. Which London-based designer label produced clothing for stars such as Jimi Hendrix?

12. The same designer made use of a selection of Indian patterned bed covers to produce full-length kaftans, worn by Mick Jagger and George Harrison, with a half-belt at the back and a neat collar. What name was given to the shortened version that would become a major fashion craze?

13. What style of sweater enjoyed huge popularity over the decade, worn by Beatniks as well as popularized by stars such as Sammy Davis Jr., Paul Newman and Senator Robert Kennedy?

14. What name was given to the most popular design of spectacle frames

in the era, with upward sweeping edges and favoured by some of the great icons of the era such as Audrey Hepburn and Marilyn Monroe?

15. What classic sixties sunglasses, designed by Oliver Goldsmith, were modelled by Audrey Hepburn in *Breakfast at Tiffany's*?

16. Which hairstyle was worn by actress Marsha Hunt on the iconic poster for the 1968 UK stage production, *Hair*, making her an instant celebrity?

17. Which leading British fashion photographer landed his first commission with *Vogue* in 1962?

18. Which British model, one of the world's earliest supermodels, became synonymous with London's image as a 'Swinging' city in the decade?

19. Which British teen model was named 'The Face of 1966' by the *Daily Express* newspaper and had garnered a global reputation as a model by 1967?

20. Which hairstyle, thought to have been the work of hairdresser Raymond Bessone, was made popular by celebrities such as First Lady Jackie Kennedy and Dusty Springfield?

1960 - 1965

SPACE RACE

1. *TIROS-1* (Television Infrared Observation Satellite) launched on 1st April 1960 – the first successful satellite of its kind. What was its primary function?

2. On 18th August 1960, the US launched *Discoverer XIV*; the Russian responded with the Zenit programme in 1961. What was the primary function of these satellites?

3. What significant political event took place on 8th November 1960?

4. Who orbited the Earth once on 12th April 1961 and became the first man in space?

5. On 5th May 1960, who became the first American in space?

6. On 25th May 1961, President John F. Kennedy made an historic speech before a joint session of Congress. What goal did he announce?

7. How long did the Russian cosmonaut Gherman Titov spend in space aboard *Vostok 2* in August 1961?

8. On 7th December 1961, NASA announced its second space programme. What was the project name?

9. How many times did John Glenn orbit the Earth on 20th February 1962?

10. *Mariner 2* was launched from Cape Canaveral on 27th August 1962, on a mission to study which planet?

11. In 1963, NASA's first five-year space programme ended. What was its project name?

12. On 15th May 1963, Gordon Cooper spent 34 hours in space. He was the last American to do what?

13. What first did cosmonaut Valentia Tereshkova achieve on 16th June 1963?

14. On 22nd November 1963, President Kennedy was assassinated in which American city, changing the minds of detractors to the space race?

15. On 31st July 1964, NASA's *Ranger 7* transmitted the first close range images of which object in the solar system?

16. On 18th March 1965, Alexei Leonov spent 12 minutes doing what, for the first time in human history?

17. On 3rd June 1965, Ed White became the first American to do what?

18. On 14th July 1965, *Mariner 4* flew past which planet and sent back photos to Earth?

19. In December 1965, how many weeks did Frank Borman and James Lovell spend in Earth orbit aboard *Gemini 7*: 1, 2 or 6?

20. On 15th December 1965, while in Earth orbit, Walter Schirra and Thomas Stafford, in their *Gemini 6A* spacecraft came within 1 foot of what?

Sixties Inventions and INNOVATIONS

1. In 1960, an engineer named Fredrick Moby from General Electric in the US was granted a patent for a new kind of light bulb that would fit into a standard light bulb socket. What was it?

2. What innovative new toy for budding artists everywhere was launched in the US in time for Christmas, 1960?

3. In 1961, a professor at the University of California, Berkeley invented a new means of organising and analysing data electronically. What was it?

4. In 1961, a former farm boy from Kansas named Omar Knedlik was granted a patent for a new, carbonated frozen drink. His idea would later be rebranded and loved by children the world over. By what name is it most commonly known today?

5. Which innovation was launched onto the music and home entertainment market by the Philips Company of Netherlands in 1962?

6. A Japanese designer named Yukio Horie from Tokyo launched a new pen concept onto the global market in 1962. His company would later become known as Pentel; what was his innovation?

SIXTIES INVENTIONS AND INNOVATIONS

7. What was the name of the earliest video game, designed at MIT in 1962?

8. In 1963, Bell Telephone in the US offered the first of a new era of telephones to its customers. What were they?

9. In 1963, a Venice Beach lifeguard was granted a patent for a new innovation that significantly enhanced life for keen skateboarders, enabling the majority of tricks performed in the sport today. What was his design feature?

10. Which new form of fast-drying paint first became commercially available to artists in 1964?

11. How was computer programming transformed in 1964 by the work of John G. Kennedy and Thomas E. Kurtz of Dartmouth College, New Hampshire?

12. What innovative design of lingerie was launched in North America in 1964, in response to the feminist movement's rejection of the girdle?

13. Which security device became available in the home for the first time in 1965 thanks to a patented battery-powered design by Duane D. Pearsall and Stanley B. Peterson?

14. What alternative to spectacles first became available from 1965, thanks to the pioneering work of a scientist from Czechoslovakia named Otto Wichterle?

15. What did scientist James Schlatter discover in 1965 that would transform the world of sugary drinks and foods?

16. Which high-strength fibre was the work of a DuPont scientist named Stephanie Kwolek in 1965, now used for a wide variety of applications including armour and protective safety gear?

17. Which video display technology was invented in 1966?

18. Which invention began to transform the automobile industry when it first became integral to car design and manufacture in companies such as VW, Mercedes-Benz, Volvo, Porsche and Saab from 1967?

19. What hand-held device was invented by US physicist Jack Kilby in 1967?

20. What technological computer device did engineer Douglas Engelbart first invent, using wood, in 1968?

1960s Children's and Young Adult NOVELS

Name the Novels in Which These Characters Appear

1. Sam-I-Am

2. A badger named Frances, in her first of seven stories

3. Karana and her brother Ramo, who leaves his sister alone on an island after he is killed by feral dogs

4. James Henry Trotter and his aunts, Spiker and Sponge

5. Sylvester McMonkey McBean, the Fix-It-Up Chappie

6. Luath the Labrador, Bodger the Bull Terrier and Tao the Siamese cat

7. Merricat Blackwood, her sister Constance and their frail old uncle Julian

8. Sir Willoughby, Lady Green, their daughter Bonnie and her cousin Letitia Slighcarp

9. Peter, a young African-American boy on an adventure in snowy Brooklyn

10. Max, a small boy with a big imagination and a bedroom full of Wild Things

11. Julian, Dick, Anne, George and Timmy the dog – on their final adventure together

12. Peter, Janet, Jack, Pam, Barbara, Colin, George and Scamper the dog – on their final adventure together

13. Leroy Brown, a curious and investigative young boy, on his first in a series of 29 adventures

14. Charlie Bucket and Grandpa Joe

15. 'Boy' and an apple tree that keeps on giving

16. Caractacus Pott and his children Jeremy and Jemima, Lord Skrumshus and Monsieur Bob-Bon

17. Ged, known as Sparrowhawk and Ogion the Silent

18. A giant made of iron, a boy named Hogarth and the Space-Bat-Angel-Dragon

19. Time-travelling Charlotte Makepeace

20. A newly hatched caterpillar and an array of snacks

Celebrity Female

DEATHS

1. Which leading figure from the British Suffragette movement died in Ethiopia, where she had lived since 1956 and had been a friend and advisor to Emperor Haile Selassie?

2. Which British writer and landscape gardener, who inspired Virginia Woolf to create the androgynous *Orlando* after their affair, died at Sissinghurst, Kent in 1962?

3. Which Hollywood screen idol was found dead in her home in 1962?

4. Which Danish novelist, best known for her novel *Out of Africa* and her short story *Babette's Feast*, died in Denmark in 1962?

5. Which former First Lady of the United States died in New York in 1962 at the age of 78?

6. Which American poet and novelist, known for her confessional poetry and for novels such as *The Bell Jar*, committed suicide in her kitchen in Primrose Hill in 1963?

7. Which American country music and pop singer, known for hit records such as 'Crazy', died in an air crash in Tennessee in 1963?

8. Which French singer, known internationally for her distinctive voice, died in the South of France in 1963 following a long illness?

9. Which African-American Jazz and Blues singer, self-titled 'Queen of the Blues', died of a drug overdose at the age of 39 in 1963?

10. Which American-born English socialite, who in 1919 became the first woman to take up a seat in the House of Commons, died in Lincolnshire in 1964?

11. Which eccentric English poet, who once wrote that she would wear Chanel Number 5 perfume only in preference to having her nose 'nailed to other people's lavatories', died in London in 1977?

12. Which American author, best known for her 1959 horror *The Haunting of Hill House* and for her 1962 novel *We Have Always Lived in a Castle*, died in Vermont in 1965 at the age of 48?

13. Which Canadian American businesswoman, known for building a cosmetics empire, died in New York in 1966 at the age of 87?

14. Which English pop singer, known as 'the Girl with the Giggle in her Voice', died of ovarian cancer in 1966 at the age of 34?

15. Which American writer, screenwriter, journalist and wit died in New York in 1967?

16. Which Hollywood 50s screen idol, known for movies such as *The Girl Can't Help It* and *Too Hot to Handle*, was killed in a car accident in 1967?

17. Which British actress, known for her role in iconic movies such as *Gone With the Wind* and *A Streetcar Named Desire*, died in London in 1967?

18. Which prolific best-selling British children's writer died in Hampstead, London in 1968?

19. Which Hollywood legend, whose screen career spanned four decades and who won an Academy Award for her role in *A Star is Born*, died in London in 1968?

20. Which American actress and wife of director, Roman Polanski, was murdered by Charles Manson's followers in 1969?

Sixties
SUPERMODELS

1. Which British supermodel was first discovered in 1960 by photographer David Bailey, with whom she later had a four-year affair?

2. What did American supermodel Peggy Moffitt wear in a photograph that appeared in *Women's Wear Daily* in 1964 that made international headlines?

3. Which German supermodel's career went global after she appeared in the 1966 movie *Blow Up*, ensuring she would become the world's highest paid supermodel?

4. Which elfin British model shot to fame at the age of 16 in 1966 and would go on to become regarded as the Queen of Mod?

5. Who was the first African-American cover model, who also worked in collaboration with artist Andy Warhol?

6. Whose modelling career was launched after her striking appearance at Truman Capote's Black-and-White Ball in 1966 and ended abruptly in the early 1970s after she developed late-onset acne?

7. Who was described as having 'the world's most beautiful face – the Face of the Moment' in 1967?

8. Who was described by John Lennon as 'hot, hot, hot'?

9. Which American model wore an iconic asymmetrical Vidal Sassoon hairstyle, known as the Five Point?

10. Which British model began her high profile modelling career in 1962 after being spotted by a client while working as a shampoo girl at Elizabeth Arden's Salon in London?

11. To which two British musicians was she later married, inspiring the songs 'Layla' and 'Something'?

12. Which British *Vogue* model was said to have lent a relatively unknown Jimi Hendrix his first Fender Stratocaster that belonged to her boyfriend, Keith Richards, who credited her as 'the one that first broke my heart'?

13. Which American model had a career from 1965 and was known for her close resemblance to First Lady Jackie Kennedy?

14. Who photographed American super-model Donyale Luna for the cover issue of British *Vogue* in March 1966, the first *Vogue* cover to feature a black model?

15. Which British supermodel had an affair with actor Terence Stamp?

16. Who was the first American model ever to walk Parisian catwalks at *haute couture* shows?

17. Which supermodel once worked with artist Salvador Dali?

18. Which British supermodel once reflected, 'I hated what I looked like, so I thought everyone had gone stark raving mad'?

19. Who was described in *Time* magazine in April 1966 as 'a new heavenly body' and 'unquestionably the hottest model in Europe at the moment'?

20. Which American supermodel found herself the centre of controversy when she was featured in a ten-page spread for Paris *Vogue* in 1973, in which she was made to appear as if she was First Lady Jackie Kennedy?

British Television and Radio

SOAP OPERAS

1. Which BBC radio soap opera was already nine years old by 1960 and was billed as 'an everyday story of country folk'?

2. Which medical soap aired on ITV from 1957 until 1967 and included actors Jill Browne, Charles 'Bud' Tingwell, John Carlisle and Desmond Carrington?

3. Which long-running soap first aired in December 1960 and featured the characters Elsie Tanner, Ena Sharples, town Mayor Annie Walker and war veteran Albert Tatlock?

4. Which 1961 television soap opera was billed as 'shopping with the lid off' and was set in a department store, starring Wendy Richard?

5. Which medical drama aired from 1962 and was set in the fictional Scottish town of Tannochbrae?

6. Which BBC soap opera first aired in 1962, set in the middle-class world of magazine publishing?

7. Which BBC radio soap opera starred Ellis Powell in the lead role for fifteen years, until she was fired in 1963 because of her drinking habits?

8. Which long-running soap opera first aired in 1964 and focussed on two warring sisters, one of whom ran a small motel?

9. Which 1964 twice-weekly comic soap was set within a corrupt town council in a fictional Midlands town?

10. Which television soap opera was set within a fictional new town and first aired in 1965, starring Alan Browning, Maggie Fitzgibbon, Wendy Richard and Judy Geeson?

11. Which 1965 soap opera was set in a block of luxury London flats and starred Margaret Nolan, better known for her role as Dink in *Goldfinger*?

12. Which BBC soap opera aired twice weekly between 1965 and 1967, following the fortunes of a second division football club?

13. Which 1966 soap opera starred a young Kate O'Mara and was notable as the first soap to use outside broadcast equipment so as to shoot on location?

14. Which 1966 soap opera was set on a barge and starred Bernard Lee, best known for his role as M in the Bond movies?

15. Which ITV soap opera was set in a covered market in the East End of London and ran from 1967 to 1969?

16. Which 1967 soap opera was devised by the makers of *Crossroads* and centred on the textile industry in a Yorkshire town?

17. Which 1967 soap was set in inner-city Birmingham and starred Errol John, the first black actor cast in a lead role on British television?

18. Which 1968 BBC television soap opera starred Thora Hird as a feisty local councillor?

19. Which medical soap opera aired on the BBC from 1969 until 1972, and starred a young Lynda La Plante?

20. Which soap opera aired from 1969 and featured Raymond Francis as Detective Superintendent Tom Lockhart?

British Children's TELEVISION

1. Which weekly magazine programme for children ran on the BBC throughout the decade every Monday evening from its first airing in 1958 and from 1962 until 1972, hosted by Valerie Singleton with a dog named Petra?

2. Which drama series for children aired in 1960 starring *Take The High Road* and *Coronation Street* actor, Kenneth Watson?

3. Which weekly children's programme was hosted by Eamonn Andrews until 1964 and aired on Fridays at 5 o'clock?

4. Which weekly drama series for a younger audience ran from 1960, featuring the daring exploits of a Detective Air Inspector?

5. Which animated space-age cartoon first aired in 1965 and depicted the adventures of an alien, 'with propellers on his heels, antennas on his ears, he's a science fiction pixie from a strange atomic race'?

6. Which children's series first aired in December 1965 and over its 30-year history featured an actor reading a story to the camera from an armchair?

7. Which children's series first aired on the BBC in 1965 and featured a five-minute story with hand puppets, just before the evening news?

8. Which iconic children's programme was written by Eric Thompson and featured stop motion animation from October 1965, later settling into the five-minute slot before the evening news, enabling it to gain a cult status?

9. Which 1966 children's programme featured a community of puppets with a storyline narrated by Brian Cant?

10. Which children's programme demonstrated fun facts and experiments in a weekly show that ran from 1966 and was hosted by Jack Hargreaves and Fred Dinenage?

11. Name the marionette who lived in a picnic basket and was friends with a teddy bear and a rag doll named Looby Loo.

12. Which French language children's drama series ran in the UK with subtitles from 1967, featuring a boy and his Pyrenean mountain dog?

13. Which ATV sci-fi series ran from 1967 and featured marionette puppets as the agents of Spectrum, a global security network hell-bent on saving the Earth from a hostile race from Mars?

14. Which programme for young children first aired on the BBC in 1968 and told the adventures of anthropomorphised plants in a kitchen garden?

15. Which children's weekly magazine programme first aired on ITV in 1968, aiming to become a hip rival show to the BBC's *Blue Peter*?

16. Which live-action puppet show immortalised a chequered-trouser clad bear when it was first aired in 1969?

17. Which children's programme first aired on the BBC in 1969, featuring a whistling race of creatures who inhabited the Moon?

18. Which ITV television variety show for children was first aired in 1969?

19. Which animated series first aired on the BBC in 1969 and featured a girl who lived in a tower block and told of her adventures with her pet mouse and dog?

20. Which animated children's series first aired in 1969 featuring an industrial community in a similar format to *Camberwick Green*?

STAGE PLAYS

1. Which enormously successful stage revue premiered in 1960 and was written and performed by Peter Cook, Dudley Moore, Alan Bennett and Jonathan Miller?

2. Which farce, written in 1960 by French playwright Marc Camoletti, looked at the life of a bachelor who was secretly and simultaneously engaged to three air stewardesses?

3. Which Pinter play about a homeless man (Davies) who was invited into another man's (Aston's) flat, premiered in 1960 starring Alan Bates and Donald Pleasance?

4. Which 1960 play by Robert Bolt told the story of Sir Thomas More?

5. In which 1961 play by Samuel Beckett did a wife talk through her daily routine with her husband while buried up to her waist, and later to her neck?

6. Which Tennessee Williams play debuted in 1961 and centred on a shamed Catholic priest turned tour guide in Mexico?

7. Which 1962 Edward Albee play depicted the breakdown of a marriage unfolding over a dinner party?

8. Which Neil Simon romantic comedy opened on Broadway in 1963, starring Robert Redford?

9. Which Terence Rattigan play centred on a ruthless businessman and was poorly received by critics after its first staging in London in 1963 but met with critical acclaim in a revival in 2005, starring David Suchet?

10. What was John Mortimer's autobiographical play, first staged in 1963?

11. Which 1964 play by US playwright Arthur Miller was poorly received by First Lady Jackie Kennedy because of its thinly veiled condemnation of Miller's ex-wife, Marilyn Monroe?

12. Which 1964 play was the first written by Joe Orton to be staged?

13. In which 1964 dark farce did Joe Orton satirise the British police force?

14. Which 1965 comedy by Peter Shaffer was written to be performed with a counter-intuitive lighting scheme, which would be well-lit while the characters experience a power cut, and be plunged into darkness while the power was on?

15. Which Pinter play for six actors debuted in London in 1965, directed by Peter Hall?

16. Which Neil Simon play was first staged on Broadway in 1965 and featured two mismatched roommates?

17. In which 1966 absurdist tragicomedy did Tom Stoppard shine a spotlight on two minor Shakespearean characters?

18. Which 1967 play by Peter Nichols focussed on a troubled couple whose only child has cerebral palsy?

19. Which 1969 stage revue was created by British theatre critic, Kenneth Tynan?

20. Which farce debuted in 1969 after playwright Joe Orton's death, and was the last play he wrote?

COMIC BOOKS

1. Why were the 1960s known as 'The Silver Age' by comic book aficionados?

2. Which British comic book, was launched by an Anglican priest in 1950?

3. Which comic strip first appeared in *The Daily Mirror* in 1959 featuring four children and a dog from the fictional London suburb, Croynge or Crunge?

4. Which comic strip first appeared in *Private Eye* in 1961, satirising men from the North of England and a particular form of regional dance?

5. Which Stan Lee superhero first appeared in the Marvel Comic book, *Amazing Fantasy* in 1962?

6. Marvel introduced which mythical hero in *Journey into Mystery* in 1962, summoned by the striking of a stick on the ground?

7. Which 'Jade Giant', billed as 'The Strangest Man of All Time', was created by Stan Lee and first introduced by Marvel Comics in 1962?

8. Which female comic book character was the inspiration behind a 1968 movie starring Jane Fonda?

9. Which Stan Lee billionaire playboy and engineering genius turned superhero first appeared in Marvel's *Tales of Suspense* in 1963?

10. Which swinging and stylish British female comic strip spy was created for the *Evening Standard* in 1963 by Peter O' Donnell?

11. Which DC comic hero first appeared in *My Greatest Adventure* in 1963, a character who derived his power from radiation but remained radioactive, protecting others from himself with the aid of special bandages?

12. Which villain was introduced by Marvel to *The Fantastic Four* in 1963, and was 'Red' and set on claiming the Moon for Russia, a reflection of the Cold War Space Race?

13. Which Marvel character first appeared in *Strange Tales* in 1963, and was a product of the era's fascination with Eastern mysticism?

14. Which DC character was a shape-shifter, combining Atomic Age pseudo-science with a countercultural search for spiritual meaning, and first appeared in *The Brave and the Bold* in 1965?

15. Which villainous demi-god first appeared in *The Fantastic Four* in 1966 and brought planets to the brink of destruction, reflecting the post-Cuban Missile Crisis fear of nuclear annihilation?

16. Which metallic fallen angel saved his planet from Galactus and acquired the ability to travel faster than the speed of light in the process?

17. In 1967, DC comics introduced a fashion villain name the Mad Mod in *Teen Titans*. Which cultural phenomenon did he represent?

18. Which quirky DC character first appeared in 1968, a Frankenstein-like monster, brought to life by a combination of hippie blood, motor oil and lightning bolt?

19. Which Marvel character was the first African-American superhero to appear in a mainstream comic book?

20. Which Marvel character first appeared in *The Amazing Spider-Man* in 1969, and was a brilliant but poor African-American inventor, driven to crime in order to survive?

The Summer

OLYMPICS

1. Where did the 1960 Summer Olympics take place?

2. Who won gold in the lightweight boxing category?

3. What was particularly striking about US swimmer, Jeff Farrell's two gold medal wins at the 1960 Games?

4. Which European royal won a gold medal for sailing at the 1960 Summer Games?

5. The 1960 Summer Games were the first to have been televised on which continent?

6. Where were the 1964 Summer Games held?

7. Which nation was barred from participating in the 1964 Summer Olympics and why?

8. What technological breakthrough enabled the 1964 Summer Games to be broadcast internationally without the need for tapes to be flown overseas?

9. Why were the Tokyo Games held in October not August or September?

10. What was notable about 19-year-old Yoshinori Sakai, chosen to carry the Olympic flame?

11. What did Ethiopian marathon runner, Abebe Bikila, achieve at the 1964 Summer Games?

12. Which British athlete won the womens' 800 metres at the 1964 Games?

13. Which US boxer won the heavyweight gold medal at the 1964 Games?

14. Where were the 1968 Summer Olympics held?

15. Which historic journey was recreated in the route taken by the Olympic torch relay?

16. In one of the Olympic's most iconic moments, how did black US athletes Tommie Smith and John Carlos participate in their medal ceremony, and how did the Australian silver medallist, Peter Norman, support them?

17. What action was taken by the International Olympic Committee in response to Smith and Carlos' stance?

18. What factor, unique to the 1968 Summer Games, contributed significantly to the number of records set in track and field events?

19. Which high jump athlete won gold and set a new standard technique for the event?

20. What Olympic first was set by Swedish pentathlete, Hans-Gunnar Liljenwall?

60s Icons

MARTIN LUTHER KING

1. Martin Luther King was an ordained Minister of which Church?

2. In 1955, Martin Luther King led a protest movement in Montgomery, Alabama, prompted by the actions of an African-American woman named Rosa Parks. What was the movement and what was it campaigning for?

3. In 1963, King organised a peaceful march on the US capital. With which inspirational speech did he address those gathered at the rally?

4. What was the rally in Washington DC campaigning for?

5. Which landmark civil rights legislation was brought into effect in 1964 as a result of the March on Washington?

6. Which accolade was bestowed on King in 1964 in response to his advocacy for nonviolent protest?

7. What incident in 1965, named 'Bloody Sunday', was a turning point in the Civil Rights Movement, garnering widespread support for change from across the US?

8. In 1967, King finally agreed to speak out on an issue unrelated to the Civil Rights Movement, about which he had long felt concern. What was it?

9. What did King describe as 'the greatest purveyor of violence in the world today'?

10. *The New York Times* ran a headline referring to the 1967 speech as 'Dr King's . . .' what?

11. In the last year of his life, King spoke more widely on political issues in line with his increasingly socialist principles. He said in one speech, ' . . . something is wrong with . . .', what?

12. To which US city did King fly on 9th March 1968, where he would make the last public address of his life?

13. What incident caused his flight to be delayed?

14. When addressing a rally on 3rd April 1968, King referred to the threats on his life and warned of 'difficult days ahead'. But he added, 'it doesn't matter with me now.' What reason did he give for being calm in the face of death threats?

15. He reassured the crowd that what lay ahead?

16. King's last words before his assassination were to a musician due to play at an event that evening. What did King ask him to play?

17. Where was Martin Luther King assassinated on the evening of 4th April 1968?

18. Who was charged with King's murder two months after his death?

19. He confessed upon arrest, and then withdrew his confession after three days. Why did he never stand trial?

20. What landmark Civil Rights legislation was passed days after King's assassination?

Born in the 1960s - Celebrity

1. Which British actor, known for his Academy Award-winning role in Steven Spielberg's *Bridge of Spies*, was born in Kent in 1960?

2. Which American actor, known for movies such as *Sex, Lies and Videotape* and for his role as Robert California in the US version of *The Office*, was born in Boston, Massachusetts in 1960?

3. Which British actor, known for his iconic 'wet shirt' scene, was born in Hampshire in 1960?

4. Which member of the British ska band, Madness, was born in Hastings in 1961?

5. Which British footballer, who played for the England team for ten years from 1986 to 1996 and was also the caretaker manager of Newcastle United in 2010, was born in Northumberland in 1961?

6. Which British New Romantic, who had a huge pop career in the 1980s, was born in London in 1961?

7. Which singer-songwriter, best known as a member of the US rock band, Guns 'n' Roses, was born in Indiana in 1962?

8. Which British marathon-running stand-up comedian was born in what is now Yemen in 1962?

9. Which American rock band frontman and songwriter was born 'John Francis Bongiovi' in New Jersey in 1962?

10. Which British award-winning singer-songwriter was born 'Olusegun Olumide Adeola Samuel' in London in 1963?

11. Which American movie director, known for movies such as *Reservoir Dogs* and *Pulp Fiction*, was born in Knoxville in 1963?

12. Which television chat show host was born in Dublin in 1963?

13. Which member of the Osmond family was born in California in 1963?

14. Which versatile Hollywood star, known for his Academy Award nominated roles as a diverse range of characters, was born in Kentucky in 1963?

15. Which British comedian, actor and musician, known for his role in the television comedy series, *Black Books*, was born in Bath in 1964?

16. Which former *Doctor Who* was born in Salford in 1964?

17. Which former British football player turned actor was born in Watford in 1965?

18. Which Swedish tennis player, winner of six Grand Slam titles and ranked within the world's top ten seeded players for a decade, was born in Västervik, Sweden in 1966?

19. Which leading member of the Liberal Democrat Party was born in Chalfont St Giles in 1967?

20. Which James Bond star was born in Chester in 1968?

Celebrity Male

DEATHS

1. Which American rockabilly star died in a taxi in Chippenham, Wiltshire during a UK tour in 1960?

2. Which Welsh politician, former Minister for Health and founder of the National Health Service, died in 1960?

3. Which Austrian quantum physicist, known for his cat-based thought-experiment exploring the Copenhagen interpretation of quantum mechanics, died in Vienna in 1961?

4. Which ukulele-loving Lancashire actor, singer and comedian died in hospital in 1961?

5. Which American screen idol, known for his role in movies such as *For Whom the Bell Tolls* and *High Noon*, died in Los Angeles in 1961?

6. Which British music hall star, known as 'The Cheeky Chappie', died in his beloved hometown, Brighton, 1963?

7. Which Irish-born novelist, known for his series of allegorical fantasy adventure novels for children, died in 1963?

8. Which American country music singer, known for hit records such as 'I Love You Because' and 'He'll Have To Go', was killed in a private airplane crash in Tennessee in 1964?

9. Which British novelist and former Naval Intelligence Officer, known for his series of spy thrillers, died in Canterbury in 1964?

10. Which American-born naturalised English writer and playwright, regarded as one of the greatest poets of the twentieth century, died in London in 1965?

11. Which former British Prime Minister died in London at the age of 90 in 1965?

12. Which British comic actor, known and loved the world over as one half of an iconic comedy duo, died in Santa Monica in 1965?

13. Which British speed record breaker died on Coniston Water in the Lake District in 1967?

14. Which American physicist, often referred to as the 'Father of the Atomic Bomb' because of his involvement in the Manhattan Project, died in Princeton in 1967?

15. Which star of Hollywood's Golden Age, known for co-starring with Katherine Hepburn in movies such as *Woman of the Year*, died in Beverly Hills in 1967?

16. Which Soviet cosmonaut, who made history in 1961, died in an air crash in 1968?

17. Which Nobel Prize-winning American Civil Rights activist was assassinated in 1968?

18. Which English radio and television actor and comedian, known for his partnership with actor Sid James, died in Sydney, Australia in 1968?

19. Which British actor, known for his role in horror movies and particularly for his role as Frankenstein's monster, died in Sussex in 1969?

20. Which British musician, member of The Rolling Stones, died in 1969?

Movies of the 1960s

1. Which 1960 thriller starred Anthony Perkins and Janet Leigh?

2. The movie was adapted from a 1959 novel of the same name. Who was the author?

3. How did Marion Crane happen upon $40,000?

4. What was the name of the motel to which Marion checked in?

5. Which character from the movie says, 'A boy's best friend is his mother'?

6. Which 1963 movie starred Tippi Hedren, Rod Taylor and Jessica Tandy?

7. The movie was adapted for the screen from a 1952 short story written by which British writer?

8. In which small, coastal Californian town was the movie set?

9. Finish the movie's tagline: 'And remember, the next scream you hear could be . . .'

10. What special effect heightened audience tension as they left the movie's London premiere at the Odeon, Leicester Square?

11. Which 1964 thriller starred Tippi Hedren and Sean Connery?

12. The female lead character is depicted as an habitual criminal. What was her criminal MO?

13. Which former Hollywood icon, turned European princess, did Hitchcock want to play the lead?

14. Hitchcock famously disliked outdoor shoots and working on location. How did he overcome this for the scenes in which the female lead character rode horseback?

15. Hitchcock appeared in a cameo role in each of his thrillers. Where did he appear in this movie?

16. Which 1966 thriller had Cold War espionage as its setting?

17. Who were the lead actors in the movie?

18. Which 1969 movie was set against the Cuban Missile Crisis?

19. What real-life incident in 1962 inspired French writer, Leon Uris, to write the novel on which Hitchcock's movie was based?

20. The movie starred American actor, John Forsythe. For which popular 1970s television crime series was Forsythe famous, despite never appearing on screen?

1966-1969

1. What first did the Soviet space probe *Luna 9* achieve on 3rd February 1966?

2. In April 1966, *Luna 10* was the first spacecraft to do what?

3. What was the name of the first NASA spacecraft to soft-land on the Moon?

4. On 1st March 1966, the Soviet *Venus 3* became the first spacecraft to impact Venus. What was its Russian name?

5. In 1967, what did *Apollo 1* and the Soviet *Soyuz 1* have in common?

6. What was the first manned Apollo mission?

7. Which Apollo crew made the first live TV broadcast from space during a manned space flight?

8. What was unusual about the *Apollo 7* splashdown in the Atlantic Ocean?

9. What happened to 34-year-old cosmonaut Yuri Gagarin on 27th March 1968?

10. How long did it take *Apollo 8* to travel to the Moon: 3 days, 9 days or 17 days?

11. On 24th December 1968, astronaut William Anders took one of the most iconic photographs in human history. What was its subject?

12. The crew of *Apollo 8* were given three identical miniature presents for their Christmas Day in space, but they brought them back to Earth unopened, where they remain among the rarest of space collectibles. What are they?

13. Which part of the Moon, never before seen directly by humans, did the crew of *Apollo 8* observe?

14. During their television broadcast as they approached lunar sunrise, the *Apollo 8* crew read in turn the opening lines of which book?

15. Which Apollo mission conducted the first manned flight test of the Lunar Module?

16. What was special about the crew of *Apollo 10* and *Apollo 11*?

17. Which was the first manned mission launched on a Saturn V rocket?

18. How many F-1 rocket engines did the launch stage of the Saturn V rocket have?

19. During the Apollo 10 mission, what were nicknamed Snoopy and Charlie Brown?

20. During the Apollo 10 mission, how close to the lunar surface did astronauts Thomas Stafford and Eugene Cernan descend inside the Lunar Module: 14 kilometres, 1 kilometre or 585 metres?

Born in the 1960s – Celebrity

WOMEN

1. Which American actress, known for her roles in movies such as *The Hand That Rocks the Cradle, The Hours* and *Crazy, Stupid Love* was born in North Carolina in 1960?

2. Which *Dirty Dancing* star was born in New York in 1960?

3. Which British actress, known for movies such as *Orlando* and *We Need to Talk About Kevin*, was born in London in 1960?

4. Which Irish singer-songwriter, known for her number one hit 'Orinoco Flow (Sail Away)', was born in County Donegal in 1951?

5. Which British singer-songwriter, formerly known as 'Alf', was born in Billericay, Essex, in 1961?

6. Which American singer, best known for hits such as 'All I Wanna Do' and 'If It Makes You Happy', was born in Missouri in 1962?

7. Which British writer, best known for her dystopian series *Noughts and Crosses* for young adults, was born in London in 1962?

8. Which late and widely acclaimed American vocalist, known for hits such as 'Fields of Gold' and 'Over the Rainbow', was born in Washington DC in 1963?

9. Which late British actress, from an English acting dynasty, was born in London in 1963?

10. Which American actress, known for her role in movies such as *What Women Want*, was born in California in 1963?

11. Which Danish-born Italian actress, known for her marriage to Sylvester Stallone, was born in Copenhagen in 1963?

12. Which American actress, granddaughter of Hollywood legend, Henry Fonda, was born in Los Angeles in 1964?

13. Which American politician, the former Governor of Alaska, was born in Idaho in 1964?

14. Which French actress, known for her role in movies such as *The Unbearable Lightness of Being* and *The English Patient*, was born in Paris in 1964?

15. Which Swedish-born singer, known for records such as 'Manchild', was born in Stockholm in 1964?

16. Which former commoner and PR executive, now a member of the British Royal Family was born in Oxford in 1965?

17. Which *Sex and the City* star was born in Ohio in 1965?

18. Which American supermodel, formerly married to Richard Gere, was born in Illinois in 1966?

19. Which American singer, daughter of one of the most iconic male vocalists of the 1950s and 60s, was born in Memphis in 1968?

20. Which Hollywood star, known for her role in movies such as *The Shipping News* and *Notes on a Scandal*, was born in Melbourne, Australia in 1969?

Hits of the Sixties

MOTOWN

1. Which US female vocal group had a hit in 1961 with 'Please Mr Postman'?

2. Berry Gordy's earliest big successes was with a band that released the 1963 hit 'You Really Got a Hold On Me'. What was the band?

3. What was the first No. 1 hit in the US in 1964 for The Supremes, which reached No. 3 in the UK charts?

4. What was The Supremes' first UK No. 1, also released in 1964?

5. Which 1964 hit became a signature tune for Motown's Mary Wells?

6. Which 1964 hit became a signature tune for Martha and the Vandellas?

7. Who had a hit in 1965 with 'I Just Can't Help Myself (Sugar Pie, Honey Bunch)'?

8. Who found it 'Sweet . . . To Be Loved By You' in 1965?

9. Which band had a hit in 1965 with 'The Tracks of My Tears', written by Smokey Robinson?

10. In 1966, which singer, an elder brother of one of The Temptations, pondered 'What Becomes of the Brokenhearted'?

11. What song was the last top ten hit for Martha and the Vandellas in 1966?

12. Who had a hit in 1966 with 'You Can't Hurry Love'?

13. Which 1966 Supremes hit began with the lines, 'Set me free why don't you baby? Get out my life why don't you baby?'

14. Which record was a hit for Smokey Robinson and the Miracles in 1967?

15. What was Stevie Wonder's highest chart hit in the UK in 1968, in which he vowed, 'I won't let sorrow hurt me, not like it's hurt me before'?

16. Who had a hit in 1968 with 'The End of Our Road'?

17. Who sang, 'I Can't Get Next to You' in 1969?

18. Which Motown artists teamed up in 1969 to record, 'I'm Gonna Make You Love Me'?

19. Who wondered, 'What Does it Take (To Win Your Love)' in 1969?

20. In 1969, who had a hit with a cover of the Motown track, 'Too Busy Thinking About My Baby', which had been recorded earlier in the decade by The Temptations and by Jimmy Ruffin?

Science Fiction and Dystopian

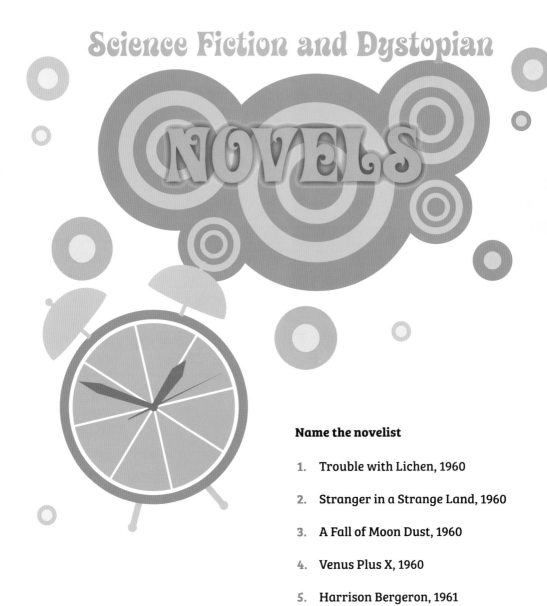

NOVELS

Name the novelist

1. Trouble with Lichen, 1960

2. Stranger in a Strange Land, 1960

3. A Fall of Moon Dust, 1960

4. Venus Plus X, 1960

5. Harrison Bergeron, 1961

SCIENCE FICTION AND DYSTOPIAN NOVELS

Sixties Solo Artists

No. 1 Hits

Name the singer most associated with the song

1. 'Starry Eyed'

2. 'Why'

3. 'Poor Me'

4. 'Running Bear'

5. 'My Old Man's a Dustman'

6. 'Tell Laura I Love Her'

7. 'Only the Lonely (Know How I Feel)'

8. 'It's Now Or Never'

9. 'Poetry in Motion'

10. 'Sailor'

11. 'Walkin' Back to Happiness'

12. 'I Can't Stop Loving You'

SIXTIES SOLO ARTISTS – NO. 1 HITS

13. 'I Remember You'

14. '(You're the) Devil In Disguise'

15. 'Anyone Who Had a Heart'

16. 'It's Over'

17. '(There's) Always Something There to Remind Me'

18. 'It's Not Unusual'

19. 'King of the Road'

20. 'Tears'

21. 'These Boots Are Made For Walkin''

22. 'You Don't Have to Say You Love Me'

23. 'Strangers in the Night'

24. 'This Is My Song'

25. 'The Last Waltz'

26. 'What a Wonderful World'

27. 'Those Were the Days'

28. 'Where Do You Go To My Lovely'

29. 'I Heard it Through the Grapevine'

30. 'Dizzy'

31. 'Three Steps to Heaven'

32. 'On the Rebound'

33. 'Runaway'

34. 'San Francisco (Be Sure to Wear Flowers in Your Hair)'

35. 'You Don't Know'

36. 'Confessin' (That I Love You)'

37. 'Oh, Pretty Woman'

38. 'Distant Drums'

39. 'Puppet on a String'

40. 'The Ballad of Bonnie and Clyde'

1960s Movies

MUSICALS

Name the musical in which the song appears

1. 'Wooden Heart, Elvis Presley'

2. 'I Love Paris, Frank Sinatra and Maurice Chevalier'

3. 'It's a Perfect Relationship, Judy Holliday'

4. 'Tonight, Natalie Wood and Richard Beymer'

5. 'Slow Twistin', Chubby Checker and Dee Dee Sharp'

6. 'Let Me Entertain You, Ann Jillian and Morgan Brittany'

7. 'Jolly Holiday, Dick Van Dyke and Julie Andrews'

8. 'On the Street Where You Live, Jeremy Brett'

9. 'Put on a Happy Face, Dick Van Dyke'

10. 'Beach Party Tonight, Frankie Avalon and Annette Funicello'

11. 'Can't Buy Me Love, The Beatles'

12. 'I Ain't Down Yet, Debbie Reynolds'

13. 'The Yellow Rose of Texas, Elvis Presley'

14. 'Barefoot Ballad, Elvis Presley and The Jordanaires'

15. 'I Should Have Known Better, The Beatles'

16. 'Sixteen Going on Seventeen, Daniel Truhitte and Charmian Carr'

17. 'The Ballad of Cat Ballou, Stubby Kaye and Nat King Cole'

18. 'I Wonder What The King Is Doing Tonight, Richard Harris'

19. 'Trust in Me, Sterling Holloway'

20. 'Talk to the Animals, Rex Harrison'

21. 'Flash, Bang, Wallop, Tommy Steele'

22. 'I'll Always Be Irish, Tommy Steele'

23. 'Baby Face, Julie Andrews'

24. 'I Am the Walrus, The Beatles'

25. 'Hushabye Mountain, Dick Van Dyke and Sally Ann Howes'

26. 'People, Barbra Streisand'

27. 'Boy For Sale, Harry Seacombe'

28. 'How Are Things in Glocca Morra, Petula Clark'

29. 'Before the Parade Passes By, Barbra Streisand'

30. 'Roses of Picardy, Maggie Smith'

Sixties No. 1 Hits

BANDS

Name the band most associated with the song

1. 'Cathy's Clown'

2. 'Blue Moon'

3. 'How Do You Do It?'

4. 'From Me To You'

5. 'I Like It'

6. 'Sweets For My Sweet'

7. 'Glad All Over'

8. 'Needles and Pins'

9. 'Diane'

10. 'Little Children'

11. 'House of the Rising Sun'

12. 'It's All Over Now'

13. 'A Hard Day's Night'

14. 'Do Wah Diddy Diddy'

15. 'Have I The Right?'

16. 'You Really Got Me'

17. 'I'm Into Something Good'

18. 'Baby Love'

19. 'Little Red Rooster'

20. 'Go Now'

21. 'You've Lost That Lovin' Feelin''

22. 'I'll Never Find Another You'

23. 'Mr Tambourine Man'

24. 'Make It Easy On Yourself'

25. 'Keep On Running'

26. 'Sunny Afternoon'

27. 'All Or Nothing'

28. 'Reach Out I'll Be There'

29. 'Good Vibrations'

30. '(If Paradise Is) Half As Nice'

31. 'Get Off of My Cloud'

32. 'Shakin' All Over'

33. 'You're Driving Me Crazy'

34. 'Nut Rocker'

35. 'Telstar'

36. 'Do You Love Me'

37. 'Don't Throw Your Love Away'

38. 'Tired of Waiting for You'

39. 'The Last Time'

40. 'Pretty Flamingo'

The 1960s and Political

QUOTES

Who said it?

1. 'I'd like that translated, if I may.' [In response to Nikita Khrushchev's angry bashing of a shoe on the desk at the UN]

2. 'A mature person is one who does not think only in absolutes, who is able to be objective even when deeply stirred emotionally, who has learned that there is both good and bad in all people and all things...'

3. 'And so, my fellow Americans, ask not what your country can do for you; ask what you can do for your country.'

4. 'A revolution is not a trail of roses... A revolution is a fight to the death between the future and the past.'

5. 'Thanks for Playa Girón [The Bay of Pigs]. Before the invasion, the revolution was weak. Now it's stronger than ever.'

6. 'Above all, I would teach him to tell the truth. Truth-telling, I have found, is the key to responsible citizenship.'

7. 'A man may die, nations may rise and fall, but an idea lives on. Ideas have endurance without death.'

8. 'Now is the time to rise from the dark and desolate valley of segregation to the sunlit path of racial justice.'

9. 'I have a dream that my four little children will one day live in a nation where they will not be judged by

the colour of their skin but by the content of their character.'

10. 'No, I'm not an American. I'm one of the 22 million black people who are the victims of Americanism. One of the 22 million black people who are the victims of democracy, nothing but disguised hypocrisy.'

11. 'It's freedom for everybody or freedom for nobody.'

12. 'I am ready to meet my Maker. Whether my Maker is prepared for the great ordeal of meeting me is another matter.'

13. 'And the imperialists? Will they sit with their arms crossed? No! The system they practice is the cause of the evils from which we are suffering, but they will try to obscure the facts with spurious allegations, of which they are masters.'

14. 'I want to be the President who helped to feed the hungry and to prepare them to be taxpayers instead of tax eaters.'

15. 'Our opinion-makers have gone too far in promoting the doctrine that when a law is broken, society, not the criminal is to blame. Our teachers, preachers and politicians have gone too far in advocating the idea that each individual should determine what laws are good and what laws are bad, and that he then should obey the law he likes and disobey the law he dislikes.'

16. 'Maybe you're afraid of sinking. Don't think about it. If you don't think about it, you won't sink. If you do, you will.'

17. 'The most important thing in my life, its leitmotif, has been the constant and close contacts with working people, with workers and peasants.'

18. 'We have always said that in our war with the Arabs we had a secret weapon — no alternative. The Egyptians could run to Egypt, the Syrians into Syria. The only place we could run was into the sea, and before we did that we might as well fight.'

19. 'Hughie, get your tanks off my lawn.' [To Trades Union leader, Hugh Scanlon]

20. 'May I say, for the benefit of those who have been carried away by the gossip of the last few days, that I know what's going on. [pause] I'm going on, and the Labour government's going on.'

Musical Icons

THE ROLLING STONES

1. Which musician inspired The Rolling Stones' name?

2. Which two members of the band were classmates at Wentworth Primary School, Dartford, Kent?

3. Mick Jagger studied business at which London university before becoming a full-time musician?

4. 'The Rollin' Stones' played their first gig on 12th July 1962 at which London venue?

5. In the early days, which band member acted as their business manager and negotiated £5 a week more for himself than the others?

6. Name the song, written by Bobby Womack and Shirley Womack and first released by The Valentinos, that became The Rolling Stones' first No. 1 hit in the UK in July 1964?

7. The band's second single 'I Wanna Be Your Man' was released on 1st November 1963. Which song-writing duo wrote it?

8. Name the cover of a Willie Dixon blues song released in November 1964 that became their second No. 1 hit in the UK?

9. The first version of which massive Stones hit, recorded on 10th May 1965, initially featured Brian Jones on harmonica and was only considered good enough to be a B-side?

10. In 1964, The Rolling Stones wrote a jingle and took part in a commercial for which Kellogg's breakfast cereal?

11. Which 1966 release became the first single featuring a sitar to top the UK charts?

12. What was unique about the song 'Tell Me (You're Coming Back)' on The Stones' 1964 eponymous debut album?

13. In which year did The Stones first perform in Hyde Park?

14. Which album cover did Decca initially reject because it featured a toilet wall covered in graffiti?

15. In 1964, Brian, Mick and Bill were arrested for doing what against a garage wall?

16. What was Nanker Phelge?

17. Name The Stones' album that was their answer to The Beatles' *Sgt Pepper's Lonely Hearts Club Band*.

18. In June 1969, guitarist Brian Jones was asked to leave The Rolling Stones. Who replaced him?

19. Where was 27-year-old Brian Jones found dead on 3rd July 1969?

20. Which Indian Hindu deity is said to have inspired their famous tongue and lips logo (along with Jagger's): Shiva, Ganesha or Kali the Destroyer?

The 1960s and

BOOKS

Name the novel

1. Harper Lee's Pulitzer Prize-winning 1960 classic look at race issues in twentieth century America.

2. Joy Adamson's adventures with a lion, published in 1960 and later adapted into an Academy Award-winning movie.

3. Joseph Heller's widely acclaimed satirical wartime novel, published in 1961.

4. Richard Yates' debut novel, published in 1961, described by *The New York Times* as 'a remarkable and deeply troubling book'.

5. Muriel Spark's most successful novel, published in 1961, which brought to life one of literature's most iconic teachers.

6. Irving Stone's 1961 biographical novel about a Renaissance sculptor, artist and engineer.

7. Ken Kesey's tale about the patients in an Oregon psychiatric hospital, published in 1962.

8. Vladimir Nabokov's 1962 novel, structured in the form of a 999-line poem.

9. Aleksandr Solzhenitsyn's 1962 novel depicting the events of a single day at a Soviet labour camp.

10. John le Carré's seminal Cold War spy novel, published in 1963.

11. Charles Webb's 1963 novella, written soon after he graduated from college, recounting a young man's affair with an older, married woman.

12. Sylvia Plath's 1963 novel about the life, loves and mental decline of a character named Esther Greenwood.

13. Jerzy Kosinski's controversial book, published in 1965 and originally portrayed as his autobiography, but later found to have been largely plagiarised from Polish-language novels.

14. The 1966 Truman Capote non-fiction novel that depicted the murder of four members of a household in rural Kansas.

15. The 1966 best-selling novel, written by Jacqueline Susann, that shone a spotlight on US women's widespread reliance on antidepressants and sleeping pills.

16. Jean Rhys's 1966 novel, intended as a prequel to Charlotte Brontë's *Jane Eyre*.

17. Ira Levin's 1967 novel, named as the decade's best-selling horror novel, which was adapted into a movie in 1968.

18. A 1968 novel by Columbian writer, Gabriel García Márquez, looking at four generations of one family.

19. Maya Angelou's autobiographical novel, published in 1969.

20. Mario Puzo's seminal 1969 story of the New York Mafia.

21. John Fowles' third novel, published in 1969 and written in the tradition of Victorian literature.

22. Henri Charrière's memoir of his life as a fugitive from Devil's Island, published in 1969.

23. The controversial 1969 novel that made a celebrity of its author, Philip Roth.

The Countercultural

REVOLUTION

1. On 4th December 1961, The British Health Minister, Enoch Powell, announced in the House of Commons that the drug Conovid would be made 'available to all' on the National Health Service. By what name was it commonly known?

2. During the sixties, where in Soho would you find 'I Was Lord Kitchener's Valet', 'Kleptomania', 'Mates' and 'Ravel'?

3. In 1969, which British psychedelic rock band released the debut album, *Wasa Wasa*?

4. The UK underground press was launched in October 1966 with the first edition of the publication *IT*. What was its full title?

5. Which Beatles album did pioneer rock critic, Robert Christgau, declare 'twice as good and four times as startling as Rubber Soul . . . that made John Lennon sound like God singing through a foghorn'?

6. Pop artist Andy Warhol was born to Ukrainian émigré parents on 6th August 1928 with an extra letter in his name, which he later dropped. What was it?

7. Which English progressive rock band from Canterbury was named after a book by William S. Burroughs?

8. What was the name of the seminal countercultural happening that took place at Alexandra Palace in North London on Saturday 29th April 1967?

9. Which band reached No. 2 in the UK singles chart with 'We Gotta Get Out Of This Place'?

10. The notorious Harvard psychologist Timothy Leary famously encouraged his acolytes to 'turn on, tune in, drop out'. Which world leader subsequently described Leary as 'the most dangerous man in America'?

11. What was the name of the band formed by Lou Reed and John Cale in 1965, prefiguring The Velvet Underground?

12. In 1964, which artist devised the show *Cut Piece* in which she invited audience members to cut off and keep bits of her clothing?

13. What is the name of the 1967 American biographical crime film starring Warren Beatty and Faye Dunaway as the title characters?

14. The 1968 bestseller by Stanford University Professor Paul R. Ehrlich warned about overpopulation and mass starvation of millions of people in the coming decade. What was its title?

15. *Are You Experienced* is the debut studio album by which English-American rock band?

16. In March 1968, Britain's biggest anti-Vietnam war demonstration saw 10,000 protestors march on which important building in Grosvenor Square?

17. Which iconic Welsh philosopher was co-founder and president of the British anti-war group, The Committee of 100?

18. In 1963, which fashion designer was the inaugural winner of the Dress of the Year award?

19. Which 1967 film turned its leading man into an overnight household name and a bright-red Alfa Romeo Duetto Spider into a pop-cultural icon?

20. True or false: Woodstock, the fictional character in Charles M. Schulz's comic strip *Peanuts*, is named after the 1969 Woodstock Festival?

Sixties

SPORT 1

1. Who won the Wimbledon Women's singles title in 1966, 1967, 1968 and three times during the seventies?

2. Which sporting event in 1967 was the first scheduled colour television transmission in the UK?

3. Which former World Heavyweight boxing champion was killed in a plane crash on 31st August 1969, on the eve of his 46th birthday?

4. On 13th October 1960, in Game 7 of the World Series, Pittsburgh Pirates player Bill Mazeroski became the first person to do what?

5. Nicknamed 'Broadway Joe', which quarterback was widely ridiculed for his infamous Jets' victory prediction before the 1969 Super Bowl III, but was proved right?

6. On 11th January 1960, former Utah chicken farmer, Lamar Clark, set a professional boxing record of 44 that has never been beaten. What was the record?

7. In which year did British Grand Prix driver Graham Hill win the world championship for the first time?

8. Who spent a month in a coma and ended his motor racing career after crashing his Lotus during the Glover Trophy at Goodwood on 23rd April 1962?

9. Which team dominated professional basketball during the sixties and won 9 of the 10 championships?

10. Which nine-time champion won The Epsom Derby on St. Paddy in 1960 and Sir Ivor in 1968?

11. Which rugby team claimed The Triple Crown in 1960 but didn't win it again for another 20 years?

12. How did Sheffield Wednesday players Peter Swan, Tony Kay and David Layne hit the headlines in 1964?

13. Which Australian tennis player achieved the Grand Slam for an unprecedented second time in 1969?

14. Which nine-time Olympic champion set the first American record of his career in the 100-yard butterfly at the AAU Indoor Championships in Dallas, Texas on 8th April 1967?

15. Which team won the Football World Cup in Chile in 1962, with a 3–1 victory over Czechoslovakia?

16. In which year did English golfer Tony Jacklin win The Open Championship?

17. In 1961, which South African golfer became the first non-American to win the Masters Tournament?

18. In 1969, what prize did the winner of the Wimbledon Men's Singles Championship receive: £3,000, £30,000 or £300,000?

19. In 1969, what percentage compared to the male prize did the winner of the Wimbledon Women's Singles Championship receive: 20, 25 or 50 per cent?

20. In which year was the National Football League Championship Game played on 31st December dubbed 'The Ice Bowl' because of temperatures of −15°F (−26°C)?

1. Christopher Booker was the inaugural editor of which British satirical and current affairs magazine that launched in 1961.

2. What was the name of the London nightclub at 18 Greek Street, Soho, founded by Peter Cook and Nicholas Luard that opened in October 1961?

3. Which 1960s satire show was responsible for bringing together five members of the Monty Python comedy troupe?

4. Name the four comedians who filmed their hit comedy revue *Beyond The Fringe* for the BBC in 1964.

5. What was the name of the character played by Peter Cook who aspired to become a judge but 'didn't have the Latin'?

6. Why was Dudley Moore's character, Mr Spiggott, considered unsuitable for the role of Tarzan?

7. Which former British Prime Minister did Peter Cook mercilessly lampoon?

8. Who devised and directed *That Was the Week That Was*?

9. Which night of the week was it broadcast?

10. Who presented the show?

11. Complete the second line of the theme tune: 'That was the week that was, _____.'

12. Who opened the show each week by singing the theme tune?

13. Who sang an improvised topical calypso each week?

14. Name the satirical show that aired during the winter of 1964–65, hosted by David Frost, and featuring Willy Rushton and the poet P.J. Kavanagh, that failed to repeat the success of TW3.

15. Name the successful satirical television show that ran on the BBC from 1966–67, hosted by David Frost.

16. Name the three comedians who appeared in the famous Class Sketch: ('I look down on him . . .'), first broadcast on 7th April 1966.

17. Who were the two other main performers, aside from Frost and the three comedians in the Class Sketch?

18. Which double act starred in *Not Only . . . But Also*?

19. What was the name of the stereotypical upper class English duffer played by Peter Cook?

20. This same character opened a spectacularly unsuccessful restaurant in the middle of a bog on the Yorkshire Moors. What was its name?

Musical Icons

BOB DYLAN

1. What was Bob Dylan's birth name?

2. What year did he officially change his name?

3. In January 1961, the 19-year-old college dropout travelled to New York City, to perform and visit his musical idol who was in a psychiatric hospital suffering from Huntington's disease. What was his name?

4. In October 1961, Dylan signed to which record company?

5. His first professional recording was playing which instrument on a Harry Belafonte session?

6. His eponymous debut album was released on 19th March 1962 and sold how many copies in its first year: 5,000, 50,000 or 5 million?

7. During the early days, why did insiders in the record company refer to Dylan as 'Hammond's Folly'?

8. Dylan also recorded for Broadside, a folk magazine and record label, using which pseudonym?

9. Written in 1962, his song 'Blowin' in the Wind' was one of the biggest hit singles for which American folk trio?

10. Dylan made his first visit to the United Kingdom in late 1962 and appeared on a Sunday Night Play, broadcast by the BBC on 13th January 1963. What was it called?

11. What was the name of Dylan's second album, released in May 1963?

12. Which American folk singer-songwriter, activist and lover was instrumental in making him famous and performed with him at the March on Washington on 28th August 1963?

13. Which album included 'Mr Tambourine Man' and featured his first recordings with electric instruments?

14. Name his six-minute 1965 single that changed perceptions forever of what was possible in a popular song?

15. On 25th July 1965, Dylan performed with a rock band at the Newport Folk Festival. What did some sections of the audience do?

16. During a concert at Manchester's Free Trade Hall on 17th May 1966 an audience member shouted a single word – the most famous heckle in rock 'n' roll history. What was it?

17. How did Dylan respond?

18. On 22nd November 1965, Dylan secretly married a 25-year-old former model. What was her name?

19. How many children did they have together?

20. On 29th July 1966, how did Dylan break several vertebrae in his neck?

Sixties

SPORT 2

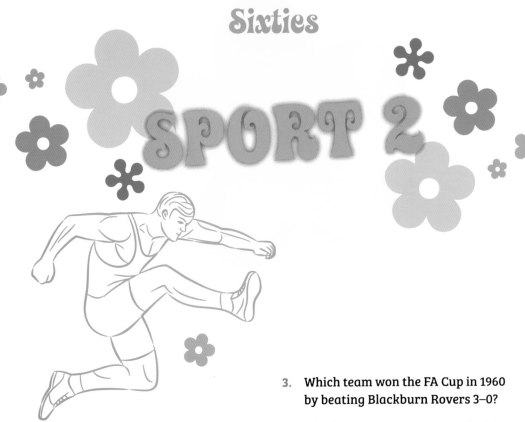

1. In 1965, who played his final game for Stoke City after 34 years as a professional footballer?

2. Name the British woman who won the Wimbledon Ladies' Singles Championship in 1969.

3. Which team won the FA Cup in 1960 by beating Blackburn Rovers 3–0?

4. Which annual race was televised in Britain for the first time in 1960?

5. Name the American golfer who turned professional in 1962 and won the first of his four US Open titles in the same year.

6. Which Scottish football team won the European Cup in 1967?

7. Which legendary Welsh fullback made his International rugby debut in 1969 aged nineteen?

8. On 17th April 1964, The New York Mets played their first game at their brand-new stadium. What was it called?

9. On 8th March 1969, what caused the final match of England's tour of Pakistan to be abandoned, resulting in a series draw?

10. Who hit the headlines in 1965 by refusing to pitch in the first game of the World Series, in observance of Yom Kippur?

11. In 1967, English yachtsman Francis Chichester completed his record-breaking solo circumnavigation of the world. What was the name of his boat?

12. Manchester City won four trophies in three seasons from 1968–70. Who played on the right wing with the nickname 'Buzzer'?

13. Who did Cassius Clay (later Muhammad Ali) defeat to become World Heavyweight Champion for the first time?

14. Who won the Wimbledon Men's Singles Championship four times during the sixties?

15. On 18th October 1968, who smashed the long jump world record by 55cm and held it for 23 years?

16. Which horse, named after a Scottish mountain, won the Cheltenham Gold Cup three years in a row in 1964, 1965 and 1966?

17. In 1964, which Frenchman became the first cyclist to win the Tour de France five times?

18. Nicknamed the Big Dipper, which American basketball legend broke eight NBA records, and was named NBA MVP and Rookie of the Year in 1960?

19. Name the Scottish Grand Prix driver who won the first of his two Formula One titles in 1963.

20. On 4th January 1967, Donald Campbell, British land and water speed record holder, died on which lake in Cumbria?

The 1960s and

MEDICAL FIRSTS

1. What life-saving technique was widely adopted by the medical community and the American Red Cross by 1960?

2. An early, experimental version of which medical procedure for sensory-impaired patients was available in 1960?

3. Which medical procedure was carried out successfully for the first time in the UK in February 1960 at the Edinburgh Royal Infirmary?

4. What new medication was made available to married women in the UK for the first time in 1961?

5. Which medical procedure was carried out successfully for the first time in 1962 by Professor John Charmley at a hospital in Wigan?

6. Which oral vaccination, developed by Albert Sabin, came into general use in 1962?

7. Which transplant procedure was carried out for the first time by US surgeon James Hardy in 1963?

8. Which medication was first made available in 1963 and has since become the world's most frequently prescribed?

9. Which vaccine against a common childhood illness was first made available in 1963?

10. Which cardiac medication was first synthesised by Scottish pharmacologist, Sir James Black in 1964?

11. In a Belfast ambulance in 1965 what was installed for the first time anywhere in the world, thanks to the work of surgeon Frank Pantridge?

12. What technological diagnostic medical procedure was first developed by NASA to survey the surface of the Moon to select an appropriate landing site?

13. What computer-assisted medical diagnostic procedure was demonstrated for the first time in 1965 at the University of Pennsylvania?

14. What medical procedure was made legal in the UK by an Act of Parliament in 1967?

15. Which transplant operation was performed successfully for the first time by Thomas Starzi in 1967?

16. A vaccine for which childhood illness was first licensed in the US in 1967 and in the UK from 1971?

17. What procedure was carried out for the first time anywhere in the world by South African surgeon Christian Barnard in 1967?

18. A team of 18 doctors and nurses, led by South African surgeon Donald Ross, carried out which complex medical procedure for the first time in the UK at a hospital in Marylebone, London in 1968?

19. In 1969, the cause of death of an American teenager known only as 'Robert R' was unknown, but would be retrospectively identified as the first known North American case of which virus?

20. What system for testing the safety and efficacy of drugs was first advocated and devised by a physician named Archie Cochrane from Galashiels?

MOVIE QUOTES

Who said it and in which movie?

1. 'When a free man dies, he loses the pleasure of life. A slave loses his pain. Death is the only freedom a slave knows.'

2. 'People don't belong to people . . . I'll never let anybody put me in a cage.'

3. 'There may be honour among thieves, but there's none in politicians.'

4. 'What drives me insane is the twofold nature of this nymphet, of every nymphet perhaps . . .'

5. 'You never really understand a person until you consider things from his point of view . . . Until you climb inside of his skin and walk around in it.'

6. 'Play conqueror all you want, Mighty Caesar . . . But neither you nor any other barbarian has the right to destroy one human thought!'

7. 'You aren't seriously suggesting that if I get through the wire and case everything out there and don't get picked up, to turn myself in and get thrown back in the cooler for a couple of months so you can get the information you need?'

8. 'Gentlemen, you can't fight in here! This is the War Room!'

9. 'I don't think it's nice, you laughin'. You see, my mule don't like people laughing. He gets the crazy idea you're laughin' at him.'

10. 'The party was right: one man desperate for a bit of fuel is pathetic. Five million people desperate for fuel will destroy a city.'

11. 'I hope that was an empty bottle, George! You can't afford to waste good liquor, not on your salary!'

12. 'You see, in this world there's two kinds of people, my friend: those with loaded guns and those who dig. You dig.'

13. 'How could this happen? I was so careful. I picked the wrong play, the wrong director, the wrong cast. Where did I go right?'

14. 'There's white time in jail and there's coloured time in jail. The worst kind of time you can do is coloured time.'

15. 'Nobody can eat fifty eggs.'

16. 'Mrs Robinson, you're trying to seduce me.'

17. 'Seventeen. D-day. We get out as best we can and make our way to the coast. And hope that the entire invasion hasn't been a total disaster.'

18. 'Now Miss Parker, don't you believe what you read in all them newspaper. That's the law talking there. They want us to look big so they gonna look big when they catch us. And they ain't gonna catch us.'

19. 'I'm afraid. I'm afraid, Dave. Dave, my mind is going. I can feel it. I can feel it. My mind is going.'

20. 'Beware the beast Man, for he is the Devil's pawn. Alone among God's primates, he kills for sport or lust or greed.'

Musical Icons

THE BEATLES

1. Which of these names was an early incarnation of The Beatles: Quarry Men, Beatals, Silver Beats, Silver Beetles, Silver Beatles, Beat Brothers?

2. John Lennon grew up near a place called Strawberry Fields in Liverpool. What was it?

3. In 1960, which band member had to lie to the German authorities about his age so he could perform in Hamburg?

4. How many Hamburg residencies did the band perform in total?

5. Who was the last member of the final line-up to join the band?

6. Name the record store-owner The Beatles appointed as their manager in January 1962.

7. Which record label rejected the band with the comment 'Guitar groups are on the way out'?

8. Who had his first recording session with The Beatles at EMI's Abbey Road Studios on 6th June 1962?

9. Which member of the band was sacked in August 1962?

10. What was the name of their first single, released in the UK on 5th October 1962?

11. Released in the UK on 23rd August 1963, the band's fourth single sold three-quarters of a million copies in under four weeks – the fastest sales in music history at the time. What was its name?

12. In late October 1963, The Beatles made a five-day tour of which Nordic country?

13. On 7th February 1964, The Beatles flew to America and gave their first live performance on US television on which variety show?

14. How many of their twelve studio albums released in the United Kingdom through to 1970 reached No. 1?

15. In early 1965, Lennon and George Harrison were introduced to LSD when it was secretly added to their coffee by their: chauffeur, manager, dentist, hairdresser, bodyguard.

16. Prime Minister Harold Wilson controversially nominated them for which award in June 1965?

17. The Beatles released four films between 1964–69. Name three of them.

18. In which Beatles film did the Fab Four come up against an evil cult?

19. According to Guinness World Records, which Beatles song has been recorded by more artists than any other?

20. Two of the song titles on the album *Sgt. Pepper's Lonely Hearts Club Band* (1967) include a woman's name. One is 'Lucy In the Sky With Diamonds'. Which is the other?

Match the Stars With the

SITCOM

The sitcoms:

All Gas And Gaiters	Pardon The Expression
Beggar My Neighbour	Please Sir!
Colonel Trumper's Private War	Steptoe and Son
Doctor in the House	Sykes And A . . .
George And The Dragon	The Bed-Sit Girl
HMS Paradise	The Larkins
Hugh And I	The Likely Lads
Meet the Wife	The Rag Trade
No – That's Me Over Here!	The Worker
Our House	Till Death Us Do Part

The stars:

1. Peter Jones, Miriam Karlin, Reg Varney, Christopher Beeny, Esma Cannon, Sheila Hancock

2. Peggy Mount, David Kossoff, Ronan O'Casey, Ruth Trouncer, Shaun O'Riordan

3. Robertson Hare, William Mervyn, Derek Nimmo, John Barron, Ernest Clark, Joan Sanderson

4. Warren Mitchell, Dandy Nichols, Una Stubbs, Anthony Booth, Alfie Bass, Patricia Hayes, Joan Sims

5. John Alderton, Deryck Guyler, Noel Howlett, Joan Sanderson, Richard Davies, Erik Chitty

6. Terry Scott, Hugh Lloyd, Cyril Smith, Wallas Eaton, Vi Stevens, Patricia Hayes

7. Barry Evans, Robin Nedwell, Geoffrey Davis, George Layton, Simon Cuff, Ernest Clark

8. Charlie Drake, Percy Herbert, Henry McGee

9. Eric Sykes, Hattie Jacques, Richard Wattis, Deryck Guyler

10. Arthur Lowe, Paul Dawkins, Robert Dorning, Betty Driver, Joy Stewart, Barbara Young, Holly Doone, John Le Mesurier

11. Sheila Hancock, Dilys Laye, Hy Hazell, Derek Nimmo

12. James Bolam, Rodney Bewes, Bartlett Mullins, Donald McKillop, Sheila Fearn, Olive Millbourne

13. Dennis Price, Warren Mitchell, George Tovey, William Gaunt

14. Peter Jones, Desmond Walter-Ellis, June Whitfield, Reg Varney, Pat Coombs

15. Thora Hird, Freddie Frinton

16. Sid James, Peggy Mount, John Le Mesurier, Keith Marsh

17. Ronnie Corbett, Rosemary Leach, Henry McGee, Ivor Dean, Jill Mai Meredith

18. Richard Caldicot, Frank Thornton, Robin Hunter, Ronald Radd, Angus Lennie, Priscilla Morgan, Ambrosine Phillpotts, Graham Crowden

19. Hattie Jacques, Charles Hawtrey, Joan Sims, Norman Rossington, Bernard Bresslaw

20. Harry H. Corbett, Wilfrid Brambell

Name the Male Actor in Both

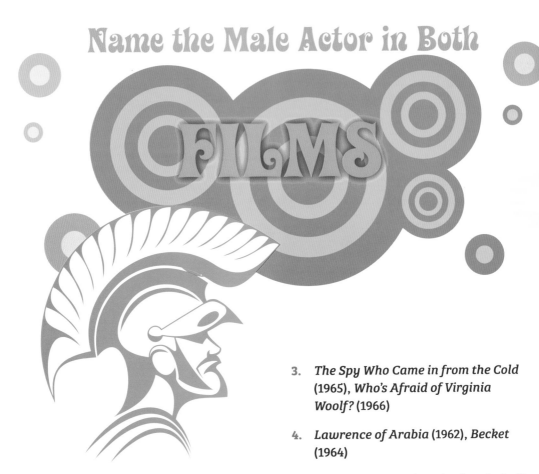

FILMS

1. *The Hustler* (1961), *Cool Hand Luke* (1967)

2. *Saturday Night and Sunday Morning* (1960), *Tom Jones* (1963)

3. *The Spy Who Came in from the Cold* (1965), *Who's Afraid of Virginia Woolf?* (1966)

4. *Lawrence of Arabia* (1962), *Becket* (1964)

5. *The Longest Day* (1962), *Thunderball* (1965)

6. *8½* (1963), *Marriage Italian Style* (1964)

7. *Georgy Girl* (1966), *Women in Love* (1969)

NAME THE MALE ACTOR IN BOTH FILMS

8. *Kaleidoscope* (1966), *Bonnie and Clyde* (1967)

9. *Breakfast at Tiffany's* (1961), *The Carpetbaggers* (1964)

10. *The Agony and the Ecstasy* (1965), *Planet of the Apes* (1968)

11. *Birdman of Alcatraz* (1962), *The Swimmer* (1968)

12. *Sex and the Single Girl* (1964), *The Boston Strangler* (1968)

13. *The Ipcress File* (1965), *Alfie* (1966)

14. *The Loneliness of the Long Distance Runner* (1962), *Billy Liar* (1963)

15. *Barefoot in the Park* (1967), *Butch Cassidy and the Sundance Kid* (1969)

16. *For a Few Dollars More* (1965), *Where Eagles Dare* (1968)

17. *The Greatest Story Ever Told* (1965), *The Quiller Memorandum* (1966)

18. *Days of Wine and Roses* (1962), *How to Murder Your Wife* (1965)

19. *One-Eyed Jacks* (1961), *Mutiny on the Bounty* (1962)

20. *To Sir, with Love* (1967), *In the Heat of the Night* (1967)

21. *Tobruk* (1967), *Ice Station Zebra* (1968)

22. *The Great Escape* (1963), *Marlowe* (1969)

23. *Spartacus* (1960), *Lonely Are the Brave* (1962)

24. *Psycho* (1960), *The Trial* (1962)

25. *This Sporting Life* (1963), *Camelot* (1967)

26. *Lawrence of Arabia* (1962), *The Yellow Rolls-Royce* (1964)

27. *The Magnificent Seven* (1960), *Bullitt* (1968)

28. *The Graduate* (1967), *Madigan's Millions* (1968)

29. *The Dirty Dozen* (1967), *Once Upon a Time in the West* (1968)

30. *The Pawnbroker* (1964), *In the Heat of the Night* (1967)

Apollo 11

MOON LANDING

1. None of the astronauts could afford life assurance for a trip to the Moon. What contingency plan did they set up instead using simple pen and paper?

2. The engines of the Saturn V launch vehicle had the combined horsepower equivalent to how many jet fighters: 20, 48 or 543?

3. As *Apollo 11* sat on the launch pad at Kennedy Space Centre, what percentage by weight of the total spacecraft consisted of rocket fuel [clue: it's very high]?

4. What was the launch date?

5. For safety, how far away from the launch pad did NASA seat its VIP spectators?

6. True or false: the Apollo computers had less processing power than a cell phone?

7. The Command and Service Module was called 'Columbia'. What was The Lunar Module called?

8. What date did the Lunar Module land on the Moon?

9. The landing site was in The Sea of Tranquility. What is its Latin name?

10. How far away from the intended landing site did Neil Armstrong land the Lunar Module: 6 km, 16 km or 56 km?

11. One of the personal items that Neil Armstrong packed in his onboard 'personal preference kit' was a small old piece of wood and a scrap of fabric. What was their significance?

12. Name the command module pilot who stayed in orbit while Buzz Aldrin and Neil Armstrong landed on the Moon.

13. What did they have to remember to leave open as they exited the Landing Module?

14. How big was Neil Armstrong's 'small step' from the Landing Module onto the lunar surface?

15. What religious ritual did Buzz Aldrin privately perform on the Moon?

16. To the nearest hour, how long did they stay on the lunar surface?

17. True or false: there was only a thin layer of moon dust on top of rocks, so the American flag could only be planted a few inches deep?

18. What was the name of the retrieval ship that picked up the astronauts after splashdown?

19. Where precisely on the landing site would you find the plaque that bears a map of the Earth and this inscription: 'HERE MEN FROM THE PLANET EARTH FIRST SET FOOT UPON THE MOON JULY 1969 A.D. WE CAME IN PEACE FOR ALL MANKIND'?

20. What is Buzz Aldrin's first name?

Name the Actress in Both

FILMS

1. *Playgirl After Dark* (1960),
   It Takes a Thief (1960)

2. *Camelot* (1967), *Isadora* (1968)

3. *Wonderwall* (1968), *Slogan* (1969)

4. *Billy Liar* (1963), *Doctor Zhivago*
   (1965)

5. *Marat/Sade* (1967), *Women in Love*
   (1969)

6. *One Million Years B.C.* (1966), *Bedazzled* (1967)

7. *Breakfast at Tiffany's* (1961), *Wait Until Dark* (1967)

8. *A Midsummer Night's Dream* (1968), *On Her Majesty's Secret Service* (1969)

9. *Viva Maria!* (1965), *Les femmes* (1969)

10. *The Killing of Sister George* (1968), *They Shoot Horses, Don't They?* (1969)

11. *Paris Blues* (1961), *A New Kind of Love* (1963)

12. *The Grass Is Greener* (1960), *The Innocents* (1961)

13. *Spartacus* (1960), *The Grass Is Greener* (1960)

14. *Cleopatra* (1963), *The Taming of the Shrew* (1967)

15. *Bullitt* (1968), *Casino Royale* (1967)

16. *West Side Story* (1961), *Gypsy* (1962)

17. *Barbarella* (1968), *They Shoot Horses, Don't They?* (1969)

18. *The Apartment* (1960), *Gambit* (1966)

19. *The Miracle Worker* (1962), *The Graduate* (1967)

20. *A Taste of Honey* (1961), *Girl with Green Eyes* (1964)

21. *Ship of Fools* (1965), *The Army of Shadows* (1969)

22. *Repulsion* (1965), *Belle de Jour* (1967)

23. *Georgy Girl* (1966), *The Virgin Soldiers* (1969)

24. *Mary Poppins* (1964), *Torn Curtain* (1966)

25. *Persona* (1966), *The Passion of Anna* (1969)

26. *Dr. No* (1962), *What's New Pussycat* (1965)

27. *Two Women* (1960), *Marriage Italian Style* (1964)

28. *The Night They Raided Minsky's* (1968), *Stiletto* (1969)

29. *Psycho* (1960), *The Manchurian Candidate* (1962)

30. *Seven Thieves* (1960), *The Road to Hong Kong* (1962)

Sixties

SPORT 3

1. The most popular sport in America held its first what in January 1967?

2. In 1961, Roger Maris hit 61 home runs, breaking whose single-season home run record?

3. Nicknamed 'The Say Hey Kid', which American baseball star hit his 512th home run on 7th May 1966, breaking the all-time National League record?

4. In 1969, who was famously kissed (and some believe, cursed) by Texan car owner Andy Granatelli after winning the Indianapolis 500 race for his first and only time?

5. Nicknamed *Der Kaiser*, which legendary German footballer and manager played his first international for West Germany in 1965?

6. On 2nd March 1962, Wilt Chamberlain of the Philadelphia Warriors set the highest points total ever scored in a NBA game that has never been surpassed. How many points did he score?

7. In June 1960, who beat Ingemar Johansson to become the first heavyweight boxer to regain his world title?

8. In 1964, fifty-year-old jockey Scobie Breasley rode Santa Claus to victory at which classic British flat race?

9. In 1963, what feat did Australian tennis players Margaret Court and Ken Fletcher achieve in mixed doubles?

10. Which football team beat Everton in extra time to win the 1968 FA Cup – its last major trophy to date?

11. At odds of 100/1, Foinavon won the 1967 Grand National after a pile-up at the 23rd fence by which aptly-named loose horse?

12. In 1969, who beat Tigran Petrosian to become the world champion at chess?

13. Who won his twelfth and final Major singles title in 1967 – a record that was unbeaten for 33 years?

14. In 1961, which team won the FA Cup and the League title becoming the first British club to win the double?

15. What was the nickname of the famous left hook that briefly floored Cassius Clay at Wembley in 1963?

16. What Test bowling record did England cricketer Freddie Trueman set in the fifth Test at the Oval in 1964?

17. Who became a legend by pitching two shutouts in the 1965 World Series?

18. Name the thoroughbred that won the 2000 Guineas in 1961 to become the first racehorse trained in Scotland to win a classic.

19. Which rugby team won the Five Nations Championship five times during the sixties (including one joint win)?

20. Which Northern Irish player was named European Footballer of the Year in 1969?

Sixties

TOYS AND GAMES

1. Which enduring construction toy, originated in Denmark, switched from wood to plastic in 1960 and introduced wheels in 1961?

2. What was invented by a German toy manufacturer and initially pitched in Europe as 'L'Ecran Magique'?

3. Which early years construction toy, designed to help build hand to eye co-ordination in babies and toddlers, was first introduced by Fisher Price in 1960?

4. What did Mattel launch in 1961 as a companion for Barbie?

5. From 1962, which US talking, ponytailed baby doll first became available in the UK?

6. Who was the UK's answer to Barbie, released for sale in 1963 for the first time, with the slogan, 'the doll you love to dress'?

7. Which working toy kitchen implement was first introduced in the US in 1963 and proved enormously popular around the world?

8. Which three-dimensional board game for 2 to 4 players was first introduced in 1963?

9. Which range of Danish-designed pot-bellied, bow-legged toy figures, carved from wood with glass eyes and woollen hair, became one of the biggest crazes across Europe and the US from 1963 to 1965?

10. In 1964, a line of action figure military dolls, marketed in the US as 'GI Joe' was rebranded for the UK by Palitoy. By what name was the action figure doll known in the UK?

11. Which board game used electronics and tested a player's physical dexterity and fine motor skills and was invented by a university student from Illinois in 1964?

12. Which pattern drawing toy, first hit the UK market in 1965 and was the design of British electronics engineer, Denys Fisher?

13. Which Mettoy toy, a merchandise spin-off from a major movie series of the decade, won the first Toy of the Year Award in 1965?

14. Which game was first popularised in the US after actress Eva Gabor played it on *The Tonight Show* with Johnny Carson in 1966, despite negative press attention having branded the game 'sex in a box'?

15. Which live action television series starring Adam West and Burt Ward, inspired a wealth of popular merchandise, including trading cards, model cars, colouring books and board games?

16. Which new brand of die-cast model cars, designed to perform tricks, were released in 1968 with a range of sixteen different models?

17. Which British television science-fiction series featuring marionette puppets dominated the 1966 Christmas market in the UK including a range of Pelham Puppets?

18. Which stereoscopic toy enjoyed widespread popularity, with tie-in merchandise from popular film and television programmes, including *Doctor Who, Batman and Robin* and *Star Trek*?

19. Which quirky furry toy became a UK craze during the decade, achieving kitsch status and favoured by stars of the day, including Peter Sellers and The Beatles?

20. What iconic action game for two players took the US by storm throughout the decade, selling hundreds of thousands of units before being rebranded for the UK market as 'Raving Bonkers'?

The Winter

OLYMPICS

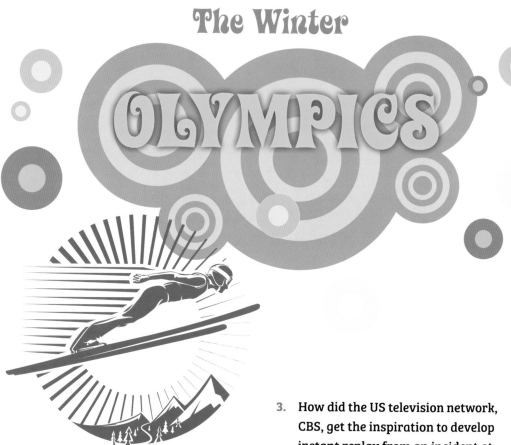

3. How did the US television network, CBS, get the inspiration to develop instant replay from an incident at the 1960 Winter Olympics?

1. Where were the Winter Olympics held in February 1960?

2. Which two events debuted at the 1960 Winter Games?

4. Which event was not featured at the 1960 Winter Games – for the only time in Olympic history – because the organisers could not afford to construct the course?

108

5. What stipulation was made by the International Olympic Committee to the host nation of the 1960 Winter Games?

6. Who chaired the Committee responsible for producing the opening and closing ceremonies?

7. In which European city were the 1964 Winter Olympics held?

8. What role did the Austrian Army have in preparing the landscape for the Winter Games?

9. Which event debuted at the 1964 Winter Games?

10. What was of particular note about the 1964 Winter Games, given that this was the height of the Cold War?

11. What tragic event in 1961 impacted on the figure skating events at the 1964 Winter Olympics?

12. Where were the 1968 Winter Olympics held?

13. For the first time since 1956, the USSR did not claim the majority of medals. Which country did?

14. Which US competitor won the women's figure skating event, becoming a national idol and resurrecting the sport following the 1961 tragedy?

15. What was introduced as compulsory by the International Olympic Committee for the first time at the 1968 Winter Games?

16. The Olympic torch relay included crossing the old harbour in Marseilles. How was this achieved?

17. What did Austrian skier Karl Schranz claim had robbed him of a gold in the slalom?

18. Why were all bobsleigh events scheduled during the hours of darkness?

19. How did the location of the venues for the Grenoble Olympics differ from previous Winter Olympic venues?

20. At the 1968 Winter Games, East Germany was permitted to enter its own team but with what stipulation?

1. What had 'a crunch in the biscuit and a munch in the middle'?

2. What product claimed to 'double your pleasure, double your fun'?

3. Which company sold Scotch Perkins?

4. Which brand of milk came from 'contented cows'?

5. What beauty brand was 'the best thing a lady puts on'?

6. What 'gives a meal man-appeal'?

7. Name the brand: 'Graded grains make finer flour.'

8. Name the product:
'They're singular, they're fingular,
They're biscuits without any bends,
They're long and little, they start at the middle
And come to a stop at the ends.'

9. Complete the slogan:
'_____ is good for you.'

10. 'Let's have Dana for dinner!' What is it?

11. Which company used the slogan 'My girdle is killing me'?

12. What was advertised as 'the purest toilet soap possible'?

13. Which series of dog food commercials featured a fat dog called Albert and a thin one called Sidney?

14. Which brand of cigars offered 'the mild Havana flavour'?

15. What was the name of 'The doll you love to dress'?

16. Which fizzy fruit drink, 'twinkles right up your nose'?

17. Which actress appeared on television as 'The Rowntrees Dairy Box Girl'?

18. What were 'a minty bit stronger'?

19. 'Everything goes with' what?

20. Complete the slogan: 'R-O-L-A-I-D-S spells_____.'

More Sixties Inventions and

INNOVATIONS

1. In 1960 *Transit 1b* was successfully launched into orbit. What innovative navigational system did *Transit* enable, used initially by the US Navy?

2. What non-dairy powdered alternative to cream for your coffee was released onto the market in 1961 for the first time?

3. What form of prosthesis was invented by plastic surgeons Thomas Cronin and Frank Gerow in 1961?

4. What form of lighting was first developed in 1962, of the sort used in remote control devices?

5. Which design feature, invented in 1963, enabled the easier opening of soda cans?

6. Which working kitchen toy for children was first released onto the market in 1963, fitted with an incandescent light bulb instead of a heating element?

7. Which British-designed lamp was first made available in 1963 and

became synonymous with the design of the era?

8. Which iconic electronic keyboard was first developed in 1964 by a pioneering American engineer of musical instruments?

9. Which popular way to serve chicken was invented at the Anchor Bar in Buffalo, New York in 1964?

10. What adaptation to skiing was patented by Sherman Popper in the US in 1965, after he developed the idea to entertain his children on a snowy Christmas Day?

11. Which useful and popular adaptation of the telephone was invented by an American woman named Teri Pall in 1965, although it was later patented by George Sweigert of Ohio?

12. What invention by Donald L. Elbert, James Faria and Robert T. Wright was originally marketed as 'ChemGrass' in 1965?

13. In 1965, James Russell patented a means of recording audio digital information onto transparent foil, lit by a halogen lamp. What was his invention?

14. In 1966, German physicist Manfred Börner patented a new system of data transmission that used glass fibres. What was the system called?

15. What household domestic appliance became available in a counter-top model for the first time in 1967?

16. What was installed at a London branch of Barclays' Bank in 1967, the first of its kind anywhere in the world?

17. What form of computer data storage was invented by Robert Denning in 1968?

18. Which invention of 1969 revolutionised supermarket checkouts around the world?

19. What technological innovation of 1969 was a precursor of the modern internet?

20. In 1969, an engineer at IBM used an electric iron to adhere a magnetic strip to a plastic card, as a means of storing security information. What had he invented?

Answers

The Year That Was – 1960
1. John F. Kennedy
2. Harold Macmillan
3. Joanne Woodward
4. The Grand National
5. Elvis Presley
6. Doctor Marten's 'AirWave' 1460 boots
7. Prince Andrew
8. The Times
9. Eddie Cochrane
10. Princess Margaret married photographer, Anthony Armstrong-Jones
11. It was the first time in British history a royal wedding had been televised
12. Wolverhampton Wanderers
13. It displayed 50 stars for the first time, following the admission of Hawaii as the 50th state in August 1959
14. He made a solo crossing of the Atlantic on board his yacht Gypsy Moth II in just 40 days
15. Cyprus
16. A football league match
17. Traffic wardens
18. Lady Chatterley's Lover, D.H. Lawrence
19. The Archbishop of Canterbury (Geoffrey Fisher) and the Pope (Pope John XXIII)
20. The farthing

The Year That Was – 1961
1. Cuba – US relations with Cuba would finally be restored in 2015
2. The Avengers
3. John F. Kennedy
4. The Daily Telegraph
5. Black and white £5 notes
6. The Royal Shakespeare Theatre, with the Royal Shakespeare Company
7. Peter Hall
8. Vote in presidential elections
9. The Jaguar E-Type
10. Betting Shops
11. He announced the Apollo programme, pledging to see a man on the Moon
12. Yuri Gagarin
13. Rudolf Nureyev
14. Michael Ramsey
15. The EEC
16. The Berlin Wall
17. Tom and Jerry
18. Private Eye
19. The contraceptive pill
20. Broadcasting began of Ireland's first national television station, which would become known as RTÉ

The Year That Was – 1962
1. Z-Cars
2. Fidel Castro, Prime Minister (and later President) of Cuba and First Secretary of its Communist Party
3. A colour supplement, inside The Sunday Times
4. Margot Fonteyn and Rudolf Nureyev
5. Panda Crossings
6. Trolleybuses
7. A Casino
8. The Beatles
9. The Chichester Festival Theatre
10. Campbell Soup Cans
11. The Rolling Stones
12. Nelson Mandela
13. Jamaica
14. Ringo Starr
15. University Challenge
16. Dr No the first James Bond movie
17. The Cuban Missile Crisis
18. David Frost
19. Concorde
20. The last remaining 1,113 participants of the Bay of Pigs invasion

The Year That Was – 1963
1. World in Action
2. Hugh Gaitskell
3. Charles de Gaulle
4. Harold Wilson, narrowly beating James Callaghan to the top spot
5. Alcatraz State Penitentiary
6. Please, Please Me
7. Massive cuts to the British rail network, including the closure of more than 2,000 stations nationwide
8. Drink alcohol
9. Lawrence of Arabia
10. Tottenham Hotspur
11. John Profumo
12. Christine Keeler
13. The Moors Murders, carried out by Ian Brady and Myra Hindley
14. The Great Train Robbery
15. 'I have a dream . . .'
16. Alec Douglas-Home
17. The National Theatre, London
18. The assassination of President Kennedy
19. Dr Who
20. The Sword in the Stone

Answers

The Year That Was – 1964

1. Top of the Pops
2. Jackie
3. That evidence suggested smoking could be hazardous to health
4. To meet the Beatles; their visit marked the start of 'Beatlemania' in the US
5. £10
6. They were appealing for help in preventing the Leaning Tower of Pisa from toppling
7. Prince Edward
8. Milton Keynes
9. Radio Caroline
10. Mods and rockers
11. BBC2
12. Habitat
13. They burned their draft cards – draft-card burning thereafter became a key feature of the anti-war movement
14. Nelson Mandela
15. The Post Office Tower
16. Winston Churchill
17. South Africa
18. Match of the Day
19. Mary Poppins
20. MPs voted to abolish the death penalty in the UK

The Year That Was – 1965

1. Ronnie and Reggie Kray
2. Sir Winston Churchill
3. Prescription charges
4. He played his last First Division game, the oldest player to play at that level at 50 years and 5 days old.
5. A maple leaf
6. Joan Rivers
7. Goldie the Golden Eagle
8. The first space walk
9. My Fair Lady and Mary Poppins
10. Liverpool FC
11. The English, Welsh and Northern Irish coastline
12. The introduction of a blood-alcohol limit for drivers
13. Wandsworth Prison
14. The Mont Blanc Tunnel
15. By 'going electric' – playing with an electric guitar
16. Cigarettes
17. The platform struck natural gas
18. Rhodesia
19. Ian Brady and Myra Hindley
20. Mary Whitehouse

The Year That Was – 1966

1. Four nuclear weapons carried on board the B-52 were dropped, three near the town of Palomares, contaminating a 2-square-kilometre area with spilled plutonium, the other into the sea. Both aircraft were destroyed.
2. Indira Gandhi
3. Decimalisation
4. John Lennon described The Beatles as 'more popular than Jesus now'
5. The Longleat Safari park, the first drive-through safari experience outside of Africa
6. The hovercraft
7. The war in Vietnam
8. Barclaycard, the UK's first credit card
9. Plaid Cymru
10. Black workers – the incident began after a West Indian employee was refused a transfer and promotion from Marylebone Station to Euston Station, on the grounds of his colour.
11. England defeated West Germany 4–2 to win the World Cup
12. The Taye Road Bridge
13. The Beatles
14. Ronald 'Buster' Edwards
15. Timothy Leary
16. A coal spoil tip collapsed, submerging a large area of the town and killing 114 schoolchildren
17. The first ever regeneration scene in Dr Who
18. Sgt. Pepper's Lonely Hearts Club Band
19. The Jungle Book
20. Rhodesia

The Year That Was – 1967

1. Charlie Chaplin
2. Cryonic preservation – his body was frozen in the hope that he can one day be resuscitated.
3. Jeremy Thorpe
4. The steel industry
5. Keith Richards
6. Natural gas from the North Sea
7. Setting fire to his guitar
8. 'Puppet on a String', performed by Sandie Shaw
9. For refusing military draft to fight in Vietnam
10. The teaching of Darwin's Theory of Evolution
11. A cash machine
12. The Wimbledon Tennis Championships
13. Male homosexuality
14. Summer Bank Holiday
15. Radio One
16. Abortions
17. Local Radio stations
18. Due to an outbreak of foot and mouth disease
19. He was the first non-white head teacher in the UK.
20. Concorde

Answers

The Year That Was – 1968

1. Percy Thrower
2. Work for an extra half an hour a day without pay
3. The Civil Defence Corps
4. He was being executed at gunpoint in the street by a South Vietnamese Police Chief.
5. A pulsar
6. Coal mining; Baggeridge Colliery was the last pit to close in the Black Country.
7. Thames Valley Police
8. London Bridge
9. Five and ten pence coins
10. The Kray Twins, Ronald and Reggie
11. The ordination of women as ministers
12. Andy Warhol
13. He sailed single-handedly around the world.
14. The first international Special Olympics
15. The ticket price for passengers on the last passenger steam train journeys in the UK, from Liverpool to Carlisle and back
16. He was the first black recipient of the award.
17. The Isle of Wight
18. First- and second-class post
19. She was the first woman in the UK known to have given birth to live sextuplets. The babies were born two months prematurely and only three survived.
20. Led Zeppelin

The Year That Was – 1969

1. Rupert Murdoch
2. The Beatles
3. B&Q, named after its owners, Richard Block and David Quayle
4. The Victoria Line
5. The right to wear turbans while on duty
6. Voting age was lowered from 21 years to 18, to become effective from 1970
7. Charles de Gaulle
8. Queen Elizabeth 2
9. Gay Rights
10. Prince Charles was invested with the title, Prince of Wales.
11. Swansea
12. The Apollo 11 flight to land on the Moon
13. Neil Armstrong, Michael Collins, Edwin 'Buzz' Aldrin
14. The pre-decimal halfpenny
15. The Troubles
16. Biba
17. Lundy
18. The 50 pence coin
19. The Mai Lai Massacre
20. He returned his MBE

Sixties British Television

1. Juke Box Jury
2. Two of a Kind, starring Eric Morecambe and Ernie Wise
3. The Army Game
4. The Avengers
5. Hancock's Half Hour
6. Comedy Playhouse. Many of the episodes spawned sitcoms in their own right, such as Steptoe and Son and Till Death Do Us Part.
7. Doctor Who
8. The Great War
9. Horizon
10. The Likely Lads
11. Call My Bluff
12. It's A Knockout
13. Do Not Adjust Your Set
14. The Golden Shot
15. Dad's Army
16. Gardener's World
17. Dixon of Dock Green
18. Holiday '69
19. The Liver Birds
20. Monty Python's Flying Circus

Complete these slogans – Advertising

1. OMO
2. Knight's Castile soap
3. Ryvita
4. Pepsi
5. Brylcreem
6. Double Diamond
7. Prudential
8. Nivea
9. Shell
10. Kellogg's
11. Soreen
12. Milky Bars
13. Meccano
14. Dreft
15. Strand
16. an egg
17. Maclean
18. Triumph Herald
19. Earth Born
20. Milk Tray

Answers

Sixties Fashion

1. The Mop Top
2. A bikini – Andress appeared in a white bikini for her role as Honey Rider in Dr No.
3. Biba
4. Mary Quant
5. The mini skirt
6. The Go-Go Boot, which was originally white, low-heeled and mid-calf length
7. The beret
8. Veruschka
9. Tie-dying
10. Bell-bottom jeans
11. Sam Pig In Love
12. Nehru Jackets
13. The turtleneck
14. Cat Eye Glasses
15. Manhattan
16. The afro
17. David Bailey
18. Jean Shrimpton
19. Twiggy
20. The bouffant

1960–65 Space Race

1. It was primarily a weather satellite
2. Photoreconnaissance (spying)
3. John F. Kennedy was elected the 35th President of the United States.
4. Yuri Gagarin
5. Alan Shepard
6. To put men on the moon by the end of the decade
7. One day
8. Gemini
9. Three
10. Venus
11. Mercury
12. Fly in space alone
13. First woman in space
14. Dallas
15. The Moon
16. Spacewalking
17. Spacewalk
18. Mars
19. 2
20. Gemini 7 – the first space rendezvous

Sixties Inventions and Innovations

1. The halogen lamp
2. The Etch-a-Sketch
3. The spreadsheet
4. The Slurpee
5. The audio cassette
6. The fibre-tip, or felt-tip pen
7. Spacewar
8. Touch-tone telephones
9. The kicktail
10. Acrylic paint
11. They invented BASIC computer programming language
12. The Wonderbra
13. Home-use smoke detector
14. Soft contact lenses
15. Aspartame (branded, Nutrasweet)
16. Kevlar
17. Plasma video display
18. Electronic fuel injection
19. The hand-held calculator
20. The computer mouse

1960s Children's and Young Adult Novels

1. Green Eggs and Ham, Dr Seuss, 1960
2. Bedtime for Frances, Russell Hoban, 1960
3. Island of the Blue Dolphins, Scott O'Dell, 1960
4. James and the Giant Peach, Roald Dahl, 1961
5. The Sneetches and Other Stories, Dr Seuss, 1961
6. The Incredible Journey, Sheila Burnford, 1961
7. We Have Always Lived in a Castle, Shirley Jackson, 1962
8. The Wolves of Willoughby Chase, Joan Aiken, 1962
9. The Snowy Day, Ezra Jack Keats, 1962
10. Where the Wild Things Are, Maurice Sendak, 1963
11. Five Are Together Again, Enid Blyton, 1963
12. Fun for the Secret Seven, Enid Blyton, 1963
13. Encyclopaedia Brown, Boy Detective, Donald J Sobol, 1963
14. Charlie and the Chocolate Factory, Roald Dahl, 1964
15. The Giving Tree, Shel Silverstein, 1964
16. Chitty, Chitty, Bang, Bang, Ian Fleming, 1964
17. The Wizard of Earthsea, Ursula K. Le Guin, 1968
18. The Iron Giant, Ted Hughes, 1968
19. Charlotte Sometimes, Penelope Farmer, 1969
20. The Very Hungry Caterpillar, Eric Carle, 1969

Answers

Celebrity Female Deaths

1. Sylvia Pankhurst
2. Vita Sackville-West
3. Marilyn Monroe
4. Karen Blixen
5. Eleanor Roosevelt
6. Sylvia Plath
7. Patsy Cline
8. Édith Piaf
9. Dinah Washington
10. Nancy Astor
11. Edith Sitwell
12. Shirley Jackson
13. Elizabeth Arden
14. Alma Cogan
15. Dorothy Parker
16. Jayne Mansfield
17. Vivien Leigh
18. Enid Blyton
19. Judy Garland
20. Sharon Tate

Sixties Supermodels

1. Jean Shrimpton
2. A topless monokini designed by Rudi Gernreich
3. Veruschka
4. Twiggy
5. Donyale Luna
6. Penelope Tree
7. Jean Shrimpton
8. Penelope Tree
9. Peggy Moffitt
10. Pattie Boyd
11. Eric Clapton and George Harrison
12. Linda Keith
13. Linda Morand
14. David Bailey
15. Jean Shrimpton
16. Linda Morand
17. Veruschka
18. Twiggy
19. Donyale Luna
20. Linda Morand

British Television and Radio Soap Operas

1. The Archers
2. Emergency – Ward 10
3. Coronation Street
4. Harpers West One
5. Dr Finlay's Casebook
6. Compact
7. Mrs Dale's Diary
8. Crossroads
9. Swizzlewick
10. The Newcomers
11. 199 Park Lane
12. United!
13. Weavers Green
14. King of the River
15. Market in Honey Lane (later known as Honey Lane)
16. Champion House
17. Rainbow City
18. The First Lady
19. The Doctors
20. No Hiding Place

British Children's Television

1. Blue Peter
2. Mill of Secrets
3. Crackerjack!
4. Biggles
5. DoDo, The Kid From Outer Space
6. Jackanory
7. Hector's House
8. The Magic Roundabout
9. Camberwick Green
10. How
11. Andy Pandy
12. Belle and Sebastian
13. Captain Scarlet and the Mysterons
14. The Herbs
15. Magpie
16. The Adventures of Rupert Bear
17. The Clangers
18. Junior Showtime
19. Mary, Mungo and Midge
20. Chigley

Stage Plays

1. Beyond the Fringe
2. Boeing-Boeing
3. The Caretaker
4. A Man for All Seasons
5. Happy Days
6. The Night of the Iguana
7. Who's Afraid of Virginia Woolf?
8. Barefoot in the Park
9. Man and Boy
10. A Voyage Round My Father
11. After the Fall
12. Entertaining Mr Sloane
13. Loot
14. Black Comedy
15. The Homecoming
16. The Odd Couple
17. Rosencrantz and Guildenstern Are Dead
18. A Day in the Death of Joe Egg
19. Oh! Calcutta!
20. What the Butler Saw

Answers

Comic Books

1. It was a phrase coined in reference to the resurrection of pre-war ('Golden Age') superheroes
2. The Eagle
3. The Perishers
4. The Cloggies – the antics of competitive Lancashire clog dancers
5. Spider-Man
6. The Mighty Thor
7. The Incredible Hulk
8. Barbarella
9. Iron Man
10. Modesty Blaise
11. Negative Man
12. The Red Ghost and his Indescribable Super Apes
13. Doctor Strange
14. Metamorpho, the Element Man
15. Galactus
16. The Silver Surfer
17. The British Invasion – the popularity of British pop music in the US
18. Brother Power the Geek – he was so disliked he was blasted into space by Governor Ronald Reagan in the second issue.
19. The Falcon
20. The Prowler

The Summer Olympics

1. Rome, Italy
2. Cassius Clay
3. He underwent an emergency appendectomy just six days before the Olympic trials
4. The future King Constantine II of Greece
5. North America
6. Tokyo
7. South Africa, barred because of Apartheid
8. The Syncom 3 communications satellite
9. To avoid the August heat and the September typhoons
10. He was chosen because he had been born in Hiroshima, on the day the atomic bomb was dropped. He symbolised Japan's post-war regeneration.
11. He was the first person to win gold in the Marathon twice (he won gold at the 1960 Olympics).
12. Ann Packer
13. Joe Frazier
14. Mexico City
15. Christopher Columbus' journey to the New World, as this was the first time the Olympics had been held in a Latin American country
16. They raised a black-gloved fist aloft, in deference to the US Civil Rights Movement. Norman wore a pro-Civil Rights pin badge on the podium.
17. They were banned from Olympic participation for life
18. Mexico City's high altitude; no Games since has been held at the same altitude
19. Dick Fosbury, whose technique became known as the Fosbury Flop
20. He was the first to be banned following the introduction of routine doping tests (he'd had a few beers prior to taking part in his event).

60s Icons – Martin Luther King

1. The Baptist Church
2. The Montgomery Bus Boycott, campaigning for an end to racial segregation of public transport in Alabama
3. His famous 'I have a dream' speech
4. It was dubbed the 'March on Washington for Jobs and Freedom' and was campaigning for civil and economic equality
5. The Civil Rights Act, 1964 which outlawed discrimination on the grounds of race, colour, religion, sex or national origin
6. The Nobel Peace Prize
7. The use of extreme force by the police in Selma on nonviolent protestors embarking on a protest march from Selma to Montgomery. News footage of police brutality caused a national outcry.
8. The Anti-Vietnam war movement
9. The US government
10. '. . . error'
11. '. . . capitalism'
12. Memphis
13. A bomb threat to his plane
14. He said, 'Because I've been to the mountaintop . . . And I've looked over'
15. The promised land
16. A gospel song, 'Take My Hand, Precious Lord'
17. On the balcony of the motel room he stayed in every time he visited Memphis, room 306 at the Lorraine Motel
18. James Earl Ray
19. He entered a guilty plea, on the advice of lawyers, in order to avoid a trial and a possible Death Penalty. He was sentenced to 99 years in jail.
20. The Civil Rights Act, 1968, known as the Fair Housing Act, outlawing discrimination in matters pertaining to housing on the grounds of race, religion or national origin.

Answers

Born in the 1960s – Celebrity Men

1. Mark Rylance
2. James Spader
3. Colin Firth
4. Suggs
5. Peter Beardsley
6. Boy George
7. Axl Rose
8. Eddie Izzard
9. Jon Bon Jovi
10. Seal
11. Quentin Tarantino
12. Graham Norton
13. Jimmy Osmond
14. Johnny Depp
15. Bill Bailey
16. Christopher Eccleston
17. Vinnie Jones
18. Stefan Edberg
19. Nick Clegg
20. Daniel Craig

Celebrity Male Deaths

1. Eddie Cochrane
2. Aneurin Bevan
3. Erwin Schrödinger
4. George Formby
5. Gary Cooper
6. Max Miller
7. C.S. Lewis
8. Jim Reeves
9. Ian Fleming
10. T.S. Eliot
11. Winston Churchill
12. Stan Laurel
13. Donald Campbell
14. J. Robert Oppenheimer
15. Spencer Tracy
16. Yuri Gagarin
17. Martin Luther King, Jr.
18. Tony Hancock
19. Boris Karloff
20. Brian Jones

Movies of the 1960s – Hitchcock

1. Psycho
2. Robert Bloch
3. She was entrusted to bank it by her boss, but stole it instead
4. The Bates Motel
5. Norman Bates
6. The Birds
7. Daphne du Maurier
8. Bodega Bay
9. '. . . your own'
10. The sound of birds screeching was transmitted via a sound system hidden in the trees in the square.
11. Marnie
12. She would steal thousands of dollars from the companies for whom she worked as a secretary.
13. Grace Kelly, but the royal family of Monaco disapproved of the prospect of her playing a compulsive thief
14. He had the horses run on a treadmill in the studio.
15. Five minutes into the movie, in a hotel corridor, as Tippi Hedren walked past. He turned to look at the camera during the scene.
16. Torn Curtain
17. Paul Newman and Julie Andrews
18. Topaz
19. The Sapphire Affair, in which a KGB defector revealed to the US that a KGB spy ring had infiltrated NATO at the highest level.
20. Charlie's Angels

1966-69 Space Race

1. It was the first spacecraft to soft-land on the Moon (or any other planetary body other than Earth)
2. Go into orbit around the Moon
3. Surveyor 1
4. Venera 3
5. The astronauts died
6. Apollo 7
7. Apollo 7
8. Upside down
9. He died in a plane crash
10. 3 days
11. 'Earthrise' – the Earth rising above the lunar surface
12. Miniature bottles of Brandy
13. The dark side
14. Book of Genesis – The Bible
15. Apollo 9
16. They were the only entirely flight-experienced crew
17. Apollo 8
18. Five
19. The Lunar Module and the Command and Service Module
20. 14 kilometres

Answers

Born in the 1960s – Celebrity Women

1. Julianne Moore
2. Jennifer Grey
3. Tilda Swinton
4. Enya
5. Alison Moyet
6. Sheryl Crow
7. Malorie Blackman
8. Eva Cassidy
9. Natasha Richardson
10. Helen Hunt
11. Brigitte Nielsen
12. Bridget Fonda
13. Sarah Palin
14. Juliette Binoche
15. Neneh Cherry
16. Sophie, Countess of Wessex
17. Sarah Jessica Parker
18. Cindy Crawford
19. Lisa Marie Presley
20. Cate Blanchett

Hits of the Sixties – Motown

1. The Marvelettes
2. The Miracles
3. 'Where Did Our Love Go'
4. 'Baby Love'
5. 'My Guy'
6. 'Dancin' In The Street'
7. The Four Tops
8. Marvin Gaye
9. The Miracles
10. Jimmy Ruffin
11. 'Jimmy Mack'
12. The Supremes
13. 'You Keep Me Hangin' On'
14. 'I Second That Emotion'
15. 'For Once In My Life'
16. Gladys Knight and the Pips
17. The Temptations
18. Diana Ross and the Supremes and the Temptations
19. Jr. Walker and the All Stars
20. Marvin Gaye

Science Fiction and Dystopian Novels

1. John Wyndham
2. Robert A. Heinlein
3. Arthur C. Clarke
4. Theodore Sturgeon
5. Kurt Vonnegut
6. Stanisław Lem
7. Ray Bradbury
8. Anthony Burgess
9. J. G. Ballard
10. Kurt Vonnegut
11. Robert A. Heinlein
12. Pierre Boulle
13. William Burroughs
14. Keith Laumer
15. Frederik Pohl and Jack Williamson
16. Frank Herbert
17. Daniel Keyes
18. Samuel Delany
19. Robert A. Heinlein
20. Michael Frayn
21. Arthur C. Clarke
22. Philip K. Dick
23. John Christopher
24. John Brunner
25. Michael Moorcock
26. Ursula K. Le Guin
27. Michael Crichton
28. Anne McCaffrey
29. Kurt Vonnegut
30. Michael Moorcock

Sixties' Solo Artists – No. 1 Hits

1. Michael Holliday
2. Anthony Newley
3. Adam Faith
4. Johnny Preston
5. Lonnie Donegan
6. Ricky Valance
7. Roy Orbison
8. Elvis Presley
9. Johnny Tillotson
10. Petula Clark
11. Helen Shapiro
12. Ray Charles
13. Frank Ifield
14. Elvis Presley
15. Cilla Black
16. Roy Orbison
17. Sandie Shaw
18. Tom Jones
19. Roger Miller
20. Ken Dodd
21. Nancy Sinatra
22. Dusty Springfield
23. Frank Sinatra
24. Petula Clark
25. Engelbert Humperdinck
26. Louis Armstrong
27. Mary Hopkin
28. Peter Sarstedt
29. Marvin Gaye
30. Tommy Roe
31. Eddie Cochran
32. Floyd Cramer
33. Del Shannon
34. Scott McKenzie
35. Helen Shapiro
36. Frank Ifield
37. Roy Orbison
38. Jim Reeves
39. Sandie Shaw
40. Georgie Fame

Answers

1960s Movies – Musicals

1. GI Blues, 1960
2. Can-Can, 1960
3. Bells Are Ringing, 1960
4. West Side Story, 1961
5. Don't Knock the Twist, 1962
6. Gypsy, 1962
7. Mary Poppins, 1964
8. My Fair Lady, 1964
9. Bye Bye Birdie, 1963
10. Beach Party, 1963
11. A Hard Day's Night, 1964
12. The Unsinkable Molly Brown, 1964
13. Viva, Las Vegas, 1964
14. Kissin' Cousins, 1964
15. A Hard Day's Night, 1964
16. The Sound of Music, 1965
17. Cat Ballou, 1965
18. Camelot, 1967
19. The Jungle Book, 1967
20. Doctor Dolittle, 1967
21. Half a Sixpence, 1967
22. The Happiest Million-aire, 1967
23. Thoroughly Modern Millie, 1967
24. Magical Mystery Tour, 1967
25. Chitty, Chitty, Bang, Bang, 1968
26. Funny Girl, 1968
27. Oliver!, 1968
28. Finian's Rainbow, 1968
29. Hello, Dolly!, 1969
30. Oh! What a Lovely War, 1969

Sixties No. 1 Hits – Bands

1. The Everly Brothers
2. The Marcels
3. Gerry & The Pacemakers
4. The Beatles
5. Gerry & The Pacemakers
6. The Searchers
7. The Dave Clark Five
8. The Searchers
9. The Bachelors
10. Billy J. Kramer & The Dakotas
11. The Animals
12. The Rolling Stones
13. The Beatles
14. Manfred Mann
15. The Honeycombs
16. The Kinks
17. Herman's Hermits
18. The Supremes
19. The Rolling Stones
20. The Moody Blues
21. The Righteous Brothers
22. The Seekers
23. The Byrds
24. The Walker Brothers
25. The Spencer Davis Group
26. The Kinks
27. Small Faces
28. The Four Tops
29. The Beach Boys
30. Amen Corner
31. The Rolling Stones
32. Johnny Kidd & The Pirates
33. The Temperance Seven
34. B. Bumble and the Stingers
35. The Tornados
36. Brian Poole and The Tremeloes
37. The Searchers
38. The Kinks
39. The Rolling Stones
40. Manfred Mann

The 1960s and Political Quotes

1. Harold Macmillan, 1960
2. Eleanor Roosevelt, You Learn By Living, 1960
3. President John F. Kennedy, 1961
4. Fidel Castro, 1961
5. Che Guevara, 1961
6. J. Edgar Hoover, in an article entitled, 'What I Would Tell a Son', Family Weekly, July 1963
7. President John F. Kennedy, 1963
8. Dr Martin Luther King, Jr., 1963
9. Dr Martin Luther King, Jr., 1963
10. Malcolm X, 1964
11. Malcolm X, 1964
12. Winston Churchill, 1964
13. Che Guevara, 1964
14. President Lyndon Johnson, 1965
15. Richard Nixon, 'What Has Happened to America?', Reader's Digest, 1967
16. Mao Zedong, who was fond of swimming, to a physician afraid to do so, 1966
17. Leonid Brezhnev, 1967
18. Golda Meir, 1969
19. Harold Wilson, 1969
20. Harold Wilson, 1969

Musical Icons – The Rolling Stones

1. Muddy Waters
2. Keith Richards and Mick Jagger
3. London School of Economics
4. The Marquee Club
5. Brian Jones
6. 'It's All Over Now'
7. Lennon-McCartney
8. 'Little Red Rooster'
9. 'Satisfaction'
10. Rice Krispies
11. 'Paint It Black'
12. It was the only original song
13. 1969
14. Beggars Banquet
15. Relieving themselves
16. A pseudonym credit used for several Rolling Stones group compositions
17. Their Satanic Majesties Request
18. Mick Taylor
19. The bottom of his swimming pool
20. Kali the Destroyer

Answers

The 1960s and Books

1. To Kill a Mockingbird
2. Born Free: A Lioness of Two Worlds
3. Catch 22
4. Revolutionary Road
5. The Prime of Miss Jean Brodie
6. The Agony and the Ecstasy
7. One Flew Over the Cuckoo's Nest
8. Pale Fire
9. One Day in the Life of Ivan Denisovich
10. The Spy Who Came in from the Cold
11. The Graduate
12. The Bell Jar
13. The Painted Bird
14. In Cold Blood
15. Valley of the Dolls
16. Wide Sargasso Sea
17. Rosemary's Baby
18. One Hundred Years of Solitude
19. I Know Why the Caged Bird Sings
20. The Godfather
21. The French Lieutenant's Woman
22. Papillon
23. Portnoy's Complaint

The Countercultural Revolution

1. The Pill
2. Carnaby Street
3. Edgar Broughton Band
4. International Times
5. Revolver
6. Andy Warhol(a)
7. Soft Machine
8. 14 Hour Technicolor Dream
9. The Animals
10. Richard Nixon
11. The Primitives
12. Yoko Ono
13. Bonnie and Clyde
14. The Population Bomb
15. The Jimi Hendrix Experience
16. American Embassy
17. Bertrand Russell
18. Mary Quant
19. The Graduate
20. True

Sixties Sport 1

1. Billie Jean King
2. Wimbledon
3. Rocky Marciano
4. End a World Series with a home run
5. Joe Namath
6. Consecutive knockouts
7. 1962
8. Stirling Moss
9. The Boston Celtics
10. Lester Piggott
11. England
12. Match fixing
13. Rod Laver
14. Mark Spitz
15. Brazil
16. 1969
17. Gary Player
18. £3,000
19. 50 per cent
20. 1967

Satire Boom

1. Private Eye
2. The Establishment Club
3. The Frost Report
4. Peter Cook, Dudley Moore, Alan Bennett, Jonathan Miller
5. E.L. Wisty
6. He had 'one leg too few.'
7. Harold MacMillan
8. Ned Sherrin
9. Saturday
10. David Frost
11. It's over, let it go
12. Millicent Martin
13. Lance Percival
14. Not So Much a Programme, More a Way of Life
15. The Frost Report
16. John Cleese, Ronnie Barker, Ronnie Corbett
17. Sheila Steafel and Nicky Henson
18. Peter Cook, Dudley Moore
19. Sir Arthur Streeb-Greebling
20. The Frog and Peach

Answers

Musical Icons – Bob Dylan

1. Robert Zimmerman
2. 1962
3. Woody Guthrie
4. Columbia Records
5. Harmonica
6. 5,000
7. John Hammond was the producer who signed him
8. Blind Boy Grunt
9. Peter, Paul and Mary
10. Madhouse on Castle Street
11. The Freewheelin' Bob Dylan
12. Joan Baez
13. Bringing It All Back Home
14. 'Like a Rolling Stone'
15. Booed
16. Judas
17. He said 'I don't believe you. You're a liar!' then performed a blistering version of 'Like a Rolling Stone'
18. Sara Lownds
19. Four
20. Motorcycle accident

Sixties Sport 2

1. Stanley Matthews
2. Anne Jones
3. Wolverhampton Wanderers
4. The Grand National
5. Jack Nicklaus
6. Celtic
7. J.P.R. Williams
8. Shea Stadium
9. Rioting
10. Sandy Koufax
11. Gipsy Moth IV
12. Mike Summerbee
13. Sonny Liston
14. Rod Laver
15. Bob Beamon
16. Arkle
17. Jacques Anquetil
18. Wilt Chamberlain
19. Jim Clark
20. Coniston Water

The 1960s and Medical Firsts

1. CPR, initially referred to as 'rescue breathing'
2. The cochlear implant
3. The first successful UK kidney transplant
4. The contraceptive pill
5. The world's first hip replacement
6. Polio
7. A lung transplant
8. Valium
9. Measles
10. The Beta Blocker
11. A defibrillator
12. The MRI scan
13. A CAT scan
14. The termination of a pregnancy up to 28 weeks
15. A liver transplant
16. Mumps
17. The first successful heart transplant
18. The first UK heart transplant
19. HIV/AIDS
20. Randomised Controlled Trials

Movie Quotes

1. Spartacus (Kirk Douglas), Spartacus, 1960
2. Holly Golightly (Audrey Hepburn), Breakfast at Tiffany's, 1961
3. T.E. Lawrence (Peter O' Toole), Lawrence of Arabia, 1962
4. Humbert Humbert (James Mason), Lolita, 1962
5. Atticus Finch (Gregory Peck), To Kill a Mocking-bird, 1962
6. Cleopatra (Elizabeth Taylor), Cleopatra, 1963
7. Hilts, the 'Cooler King' (Steve McQueen), The Great Escape, 1963
8. President Merkin Muffley (Peter Sellers), Dr Strangelove: or How I Learned to Stop Worrying and Love the Bomb, 1964
9. Joe (Clint Eastwood), A Fistfull of Dollars, 1964
10. General Yevgraf Zhivago (Alec Guinness), Doctor Zhivago, 1965
11. Martha (Elizabeth Taylor), Who's Afraid of Virginia Woolf?, 1966
12. Blondie (Clint Eastwood), The Good, the Bad and the Ugly, 1966
13. Max Bialystock (Zero Mostel), The Producers, 1967
14. Virgil Tibbs (Sidney Poitier), In the Heat of the Night, 1967
15. Dragline (George Kennedy), Cool Hand Luke, 1967
16. Benjamin Braddock (Dustin Hoffman), The Graduate, 1967
17. Major John Reisman (Lee Marvin), The Dirty Dozen, 1967
18. Clyde Barrow (Warren Beatty), Bonnie and Clyde, 1967
19. HAL, (voiced by Douglas Rain), 2001: A Space Odyssey, 1968
20. Cornelius (Roddy McDowall), Planet of the Apes, 1968

Answers

Musical Icons – The Beatles

1. All of them
2. Salvation Army children's home
3. George Harrison
4. Five
5. Ringo Starr
6. Brian Epstein
7. Decca Records
8. George Martin
9. Drummer Pete Best
10. 'Love Me Do'
11. 'She Loves You'
12. Sweden
13. The Ed Sullivan Show
14. Eleven
15. Dentist
16. Members of the Order of the British Empire (MBE)
17. A Hard Day's Night
   (1964), Help! (1965), Magical Mystery Tour (1967), Yellow Submarine (1968)
18. Help! (1965)
19. 'Yesterday'
20. 'Lovely Rita'

Match the Stars with the Sitcom

1. The Rag Trade
2. The Larkins
3. All Gas And Gaiters
4. Till Death Us Do Part
5. Please Sir!
6. Hugh And I
7. Doctor in the House
8. The Worker
9. Sykes And A . . .
10. Pardon The Expression
11. The Bed-Sit Girl
12. The Likely Lads
13. Colonel Trumper's Private War
14. Beggar My Neighbour
15. Meet the Wife
16. George And The Dragon
17. No – That's Me Over Here!
18. HMS Paradise
19. Our House
20. Steptoe and Son

Name the Male Actor in Both Films

1. Paul Newman
2. Albert Finney
3. Richard Burton
4. Peter O'Toole
5. Sean Connery
6. Marcello Mastroianni
7. Alan Bates
8. Warren Beatty
9. George Peppard
10. Charlton Heston
11. Burt Lancaster
12. Henry Fonda
13. Michael Caine
14. Tom Courtenay
15. Robert Redford
16. Clint Eastwood
17. Max von Sydow
18. Jack Lemmon
19. Marlon Brando
20. Sidney Poitier
21. Rock Hudson
22. James Garner
23. Kirk Douglas
24. Anthony Perkins
25. Richard Harris
26. Omar Sharif
27. Steve McQueen
28. Dustin Hoffman
29. Charles Bronson
30. Rod Steiger

Apollo 11 Moon Landing

1. They wrote hundreds of autographs. In the event of their deaths, they could have been sold at a premium to support their grieving families.
2. 543
3. 98 per cent
4. 16th July 1969
5. Three and a half miles
6. True
7. 'Eagle'
8. 20th July 1969
9. Mare Tranquillitatis
10. 6 km
11. The wood was from the Wright brothers' 1903 airplane's left propeller; the fabric was from its wing.
12. Michael Collins
13. The door, since a repressurised module would have made the door jam.
14. About four feet
15. He took Holy Communion
16. 22 (21 hours, 38 minutes, 21 seconds)
17. True
18. USS Hornet
19. Attached to the leg of the lunar landing vehicle
20. Edwin

Answers

Name the Actress in Both Films

1. Jayne Mansfield
2. Vanessa Redgrave
3. Jane Birkin
4. Julie Christie
5. Glenda Jackson
6. Raquel Welch
7. Audrey Hepburn
8. Diana Rigg
9. Brigitte Bardot
10. Susannah York
11. Joanne Woodward
12. Deborah Kerr
13. Jean Simmons
14. Elizabeth Taylor
15. Jacqueline Bisset
16. Natalie Wood
17. Jane Fonda
18. Shirley MacLaine
19. Anne Bancroft
20. Rita Tushingham
21. Simone Signoret
22. Catherine Deneuve
23. Lynn Redgrave
24. Julie Andrews
25. Liv Ullmann
26. Ursula Andress
27. Sophia Loren
28. Britt Ekland
29. Janet Leigh
30. Joan Collins

Sixties Sport 3

1. NFL Super Bowl
2. Babe Ruth
3. Willie Mays
4. Mario Andretti
5. Franz Beckenbauer
6. 100
7. Floyd Patterson
8. Epsom Derby
9. The Grand Slam
10. West Bromwich Albion
11. Popham Down
12. Boris Spassky
13. Roy Emerson
14. Tottenham Hotspur
15. Enry's 'Ammer
16. 300 Test wickets
17. Sandy Koufax
18. Rockavon
19. France
20. George Best

Sixties Toys and Games

1. Lego
2. Etch-a-Sketch
3. Rock-a-Stack
4. Ken
5. Chatty Cathy
6. Sindy
7. Easy-bake oven
8. Mouse Trap
9. Troll dolls
10. Action Man
11. Operation
12. Spirograph
13. James Bond's Austin Martin
14. Twister
15. Batman
16. Hot Wheel Cars
17. Thunderbirds
18. Viewmaster 3D stereo viewer
19. Gonks
20. Rock 'em Sock 'em Robots

The Winter Olympics

1. Squaw Valley, California
2. Womens' Speed Skating and biathlon
3. Officials at the men's slalom asked CBS if they could review the tapes to ascertain whether a competitor had missed a gate.
4. Bobsled
5. They warned the US that if they refused entry to any Communist nation pre-approved by the IOC, Squaw Valley would lose the right to host the Games.
6. Walt Disney
7. Innsbruck, Austria
8. They carved 20,000 ice bricks and carried 40,000 cubic metres of snow from elsewhere in the Austrian Alps, packing the slopes by hand and foot, because of a lack of snow over Innsbruck in the approach to the Games.
9. The luge
10. East and West Germany entered a combined team for the last time.
11. In February 1961, the entire US Figure Skating team was killed in a plane crash in Belgium.
12. Grenoble, France
13. Norway
14. 15-year-old Peggy Fleming, whose coach William Kipp had been killed in the 1961 crash
15. Drug and gender testing
16. A French diver held the flame aloft while he swam across the Harbour.
17. He claimed a mystery man, dressed from head to foot in black, had walked out onto the course, forcing him to skid to a halt. He won the restart but was later disqualified.
18. The bobsleigh course had been designed without sufficient cover from the sun, so the ice could not be kept firm enough in the daylight.
19. It was the first Olympics in which different events were held in different locations; previously almost all events were held within walking distance from each other.
20. The team had to comprise some West German athletes.

Answers

Advertising

1. Skippy
2. Wrigley's Doublemint Gum
3. Simmers
4. Carnation
5. Avon
6. OXO
7. Homepride
8. Cadbury's Chocolate Fingers
9. Guinness
10. Luncheon meat
11. Playtex
12. Fairy
13. Kennomeat
14. Manikin Cigars
15. Sindy
16. Vimto
17. Una Stubbs
18. Trebor Mints
19. HP Sauce
20. Relief

More Sixties Inventions and Innovations

1. Global navigation satellite system, the earliest Satnav
2. Coffee Mate
3. Silicone breast implants
4. LED lighting, initially just infra-red lighting
5. Soda can ring-pull
6. Easy-bake ovens
7. Astro Lamp (later known as lava lamps)
8. Moog synthesiser
9. Buffalo Wings
10. The Snowboard
11. The cordless telephone
12. Astroturf
13. The compact disc
14. Fibre optics
15. Microwave oven
16. The ATM machine (Reg from On The Buses was the first person to withdraw cash from the machine)
17. RAM
18. The barcode scanner
19. The apnet
20. The magnetic stripe card